Questions in
Standard Grade
Maths

Edited by
Text © 2000 M.C. Davis

Design and layout © 2000 Leckie & Leckie

Cover image © Science Photo Library
1st edition (reprinted 2006)

ISBN 1-898890-77-3
ISBN-13 978-1-898890-77-5

Published by
Leckie & Leckie Ltd, 3rd floor, 4 Queen Street, Edinburgh, EH2 1JE
Tel: 0131 220 6831 Fax: 0131 225 9987
enquiries@leckieandleckie.co.uk   www.leckieandleckie.co.uk

Edited by
Ken Nisbet

Special thanks to

Julie Barclay (design), Danielle Bewsher (proofreading), David Collins (proofreading), Catherine Gerrard (proofreading), Ramona D Dempster (production assistance), Bruce Ryan (project management) and Hamish Sanderson (illustration).

A CIP Catalogue record for this book is available from the British Library.

Leckie & Leckie Ltd is a division of Granada Learning Limited.

M C Davis

Contents

What this book contains

There are three sections:
- **Skills and Techniques Revision**
  This is a bank of Exercises designed to give you extra practice with skills and techniques that frequently occur in exam questions. Each chapter begins with topics at General level and then moves on to Credit level. Credit level questions are indicated by ⊂⋗ to the left of the relevant Exercises.

- **Practice Exams**
  Two complete General exams and two complete Credit exams are provided. These are similar in range, structure and difficulty to the exam you will sit.

- **Answers and Solutions**
  This is a pull-out section containing the answers to the Exercises and explanatory answers to the four Practice Exams.

Leckie & Leckie's *Standard Grade Maths Revision Notes*

Questions in Standard Grade Maths is the companion volume to Leckie & Leckie's *Standard Grade Maths Revision Notes*. We recommend that you work with both books when revising. Extensive references to the worked examples in the *Revision Notes* will be found beside most of the exercises in this book.

Suggestions for using this book

To get the most benefit from your revision you need to know what you need to revise. Trying actual Past Papers is a good way to find out. The sample exam papers in this book will help you find out, especially if you carefully compare your own solutions with the solutions in the Answers section. Your teacher will be able to advise you too.

Find the appropriate exercises in the main section of the book to practise your weaker skills and work through these exercises until your skills improve.

The Standard Grade Practice Exams are not long enough to test everything you are supposed to know, so you should try as many Past Papers as you can. This will give you experience of a wide range of questions.

If your exam is quite close you will have to be selective in what you cover – it is unlikely you will have enough time to do everything. You could try one or two questions from the the end of each exercise and if you get them correct easily, move on to the next topic. It is important not to get stuck on the first few exercises for ever!

If you are a borderline Credit pupil, safe for a grade 3 but trying hard for a grade 2, then you should check with your teacher whether there are some topics you have not covered in class. If so, it is best to omit these topics, at least until you are confident with the topics you have studied. Someone with a thorough knowledge of the **basic** Credit work is more likely to achieve grade 2 than someone with a very insecure knowledge of everything in Credit. Be guided by your teacher.

1. Testing your Calculation Skills

Remember – no calculator!

See these pages in Leckie & Leckie's *Standard Grade Maths Revision Notes*:

page 5

page 6

pages 5–6

page 6

page 6

page 6

Exercise 1.1   Calculations with decimals

Find the value of:

1. $23 \cdot 5 - 2 \cdot 68$ **2.** $14 - 54 \cdot 6 + 123$ **3.** $45 \cdot 3 \times 24$

4. $6 \cdot 68 \div 8$ **5.** $35 \cdot 7 \times 100$ **6.** $348 \div 10$

Exercise 1.2   Calculations with integers

Find the value of:

1. $-3 + 8$ **2.** $4 + (-7)$ **3.** $-2 + 9 - (-1)$

4. $750 + (-630)$ **5.** $3 \times (-6)$ **6.** $9 \times (-4)$

Exercise 1.3   Calculations with fractions and percentages

Find the value of:

1. $3\frac{1}{4} + 2\frac{1}{2}$ **2.** $3 - \frac{2}{5}$ **3.** $\frac{5}{6} - \frac{2}{3}$

4. $\frac{1}{2} \times \frac{1}{6}$ **5.** $4\frac{3}{4} \times 3$ **6.** $\frac{2}{3}$ of £345

7. $\frac{4}{7}$ of 92·4 kg   **8.** 40% of 386 tonnes   **9.** 75% of £5·68

Exercise 1.4   Powers and roots

Simplify:

1. $\sqrt{36}$ **2.** $2 \times \sqrt{100}$ **3.** 5^3

4. 26^2 **5.** $4^2 + 2^4$ **6.** $3^5 \div \sqrt{81}$

7. $\left(\frac{1}{3}\right)^2$ **8.** $\left(\frac{2}{5}\right)^3$ **9.** $1 - \left(\frac{1}{2}\right)^2$

Exercise 1.5   Rounding

Round each number:

1. 346   to the nearest ten   **2.** 69 835   to the nearest thousand

3. 38·54   to 1 dp (one decimal place)   **4.** 7·66666   to 2 dp

5. 39·99   to 1 dp

Exercise 1.6   Algebra

1. Simplify (write without brackets, in the shortest correct way):

    a. $2(a + 3b)$ **b.** $4(3x - 6y)$ **c.** $3m + 5(2m - 6)$

    d. $4(t - 3u) - 2t + u$ **e.** $8x - 5y + 2(x + y)$ **f.** $\frac{1}{2}(4a - 10b)$

2. Factorise (put brackets in):

    a. $4a + 2b$ **b.** $6x - 9y$ **c.** $12x + 20y$

    d. $15a + 18b - 21c$ **e.** $ab + ac$ **f.** $xy - xz$

Exercise 1.7   More calculations with integers and decimals

Evaluate:

1. $6 - (-2)$　　　　**2.** $-5 - (-7) + (-4)$　　　**3.** $4 \times (-3)$

4. $-7 \times -8 \cdot 2$　　**5.** $\frac{15}{-3}$　　　　　　**6.** $\frac{-8 \cdot 1}{-9}$

7. $6 - (-3) \times 5$　　**8.** $3 \cdot 2 + \frac{16}{-8}$　　　**9.** $-4 \times (-3) \div 6$

Exercise 1.8   More calculations with fractions

Let $p = \frac{1}{2}$, $q = \frac{2}{5}$, $r = 3\frac{2}{3}$, $s = 4\frac{1}{5}$. Calculate:

1. $p + q$　　　　　**2.** $q + r$　　　　　**3.** $r - p$

4. $p + r - s$　　　**5.** pq　　　　　　**6.** $\frac{p+q}{s}$

7. $p + \frac{q}{s}$　　　　**8.** rs　　　　　　**9.** $(r - q) \div s$

Exercise 1.9   Rounding – significant figures

Round each number to the number of significant figures given in brackets:

1. $4 \cdot 576$ (2)　　　**2.** 39 560 (3)　　　　**3.** $1 \cdot 0035$ (2)

4. $0 \cdot 000006932$ (3)　**5.** 45 million (1)　　**6.** $0 \cdot 805$ (2)

Exercise 1.10 Indices and surds

1. Express each of the following in its simplest form:

　　a. $\sqrt{12}$　　　　**b.** $\sqrt{50}$　　　　**c.** $10\sqrt{40}$

　　d. $9\sqrt{5} - 5\sqrt{5}$　**e.** $8\sqrt{3} + 2\sqrt{3} - 6\sqrt{3}$　**f.** $\sqrt{3} \times \sqrt{12}$

　　g. $\sqrt{2}(5 + \sqrt{2})$

2. Simplify:

　　a. $a^2 \times a^6$　　**b.** $y \times y^4$　　**c.** $z^7 \div z$

　　d. $p^5 \div p^3$　　**e.** $(2m^3)^2$　　**f.** $(ab^2)^4$

　　g. $\frac{x^5}{x^3}$　　　　**h.** $\frac{a^4}{a}$　　　**i.** $b^5 \times b \times a^3$

3. Evaluate:

　　a. $2^4 \times 2$　　**b.** $(3^2)^2$　　　**c.** $5^3 \div 5$

　　d. $\left(\frac{1}{2}\right)^3 \times \left(\frac{1}{2}\right)^2$　**e.** $8^{1/3}$　　　**f.** $100^{1/2}$

4. Rationalise the denominators of these surd expressions:

　　a. $\frac{1}{\sqrt{5}}$　　　**b.** $\frac{10}{\sqrt{2}}$　　　**c.** $\frac{4}{\sqrt{8}}$

　　d. $\frac{\sqrt{4}}{\sqrt{3}}$　　　**e.** $\sqrt{\frac{7}{10}}$　　**f.** $\frac{4}{5\sqrt{2}}$

　　g. $\frac{12}{(2 - \sqrt{3})}$　**h.** $\frac{2}{(\sqrt{5} + \sqrt{3})}$　**i.** $\frac{6}{(\sqrt{5} - \sqrt{2})}$

See these pages in Leckie & Leckie's *Standard Grade Maths Revision Notes:*

page 7

page 7

page 7

pages 7–8

2. Formulae and Equations

Exercise 2.1   Making formulae

See these pages in Leckie & Leckie's *Standard Grade Maths Revision Notes:*

page 9

1. Make a formula to fit each table. Then use the formula to answer the questions.

a.

n	1	2	3	4	5
P	3	5	7	9	11

formula hint: P = ? × n + ?
(fill in the missing numbers)

Find P when $n = 8$.
Find n when P = 23.

b.

x	3	4	5	6
y	7	10	13	16

formula y = ...

Find y when $x = 10$.
Find x when $y = 58$.

2. For parts **a** and **b**, make tables to fit the diagrams.
You might want to draw some of the other patterns first.

a. Number of houses (h) made from matchsticks (m).

  i.   Complete the formula: m = ...
  ii. Find m when $h = 12$.
  iii. If $m = 97$, calculate h.

b. This fence has P posts and C chains. Put P in the top row and C in the bottom row of your table.

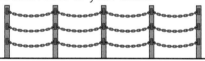

  i.   Find a formula for C in terms of P.
  ii. If a fence like this had 50 posts, how many chains would there be?
  iii. How many posts would be needed to use 30 chains?
  iv. Could you have a fence with 52 chains? Explain your answer clearly.

Exercise 2.2   Substitution into a formula

page 9

1. This formula is for the cooking time of some food in a microwave oven:

$$\text{Minutes} = \frac{\text{weight in grams}}{100} + 1{\cdot}5$$

a. Work out the cooking time in minutes and seconds for food weighing:
  i.   350 g   **ii.** 500 g
  iii. 1·3 kg   **iv.** 1 kg 70 g

b. What is the weight if the food needed cooking for:
  i.   2 minutes   **ii.** 3 minutes 45 seconds
                                (3·75 minutes, of course!)

2. P = 50 + H(Y + 3) is a formula for P (holiday pay in £). H is the hourly rate of pay in £, Y is the number of years working with the company.

Find the amount of holiday pay for:
a   John, who has worked for 2 years and is paid £5·40 per hour.

b. Paula, 10 years' service, hourly pay £8·20.

c. Darren, who's just started, earning £4·90 an hour.

Exercise 2.3   Solving equations and inequalities

Solve:

1. $3x + 5 = 14$
2. $4x - 7 = 33$
3. $8 + 8x = 80$
4. $15 = 3 + 4x$
5. $3x = x - 19$
6. $10x + 2 = 4x + 20$
7. $3x < 9$
8. $5x > -5$
9. $2x + 1 < 15$

Exercise 2.4   Solving equations and inequalities

Solve:

1. $x + 5 = 3x + 7$
2. $\frac{3}{2}t = 6$
3. $0 = 5 - 2y$
4. $-7z = 3z - 30$
5. $\frac{x}{4} = 3$
6. $5(6 - p) + 1 = p + 1$
7. $\frac{(a+2)}{3} - \frac{(a-2)}{4} = 1$
8. $y < 2y + 12$
9. $2c + 5 > 3c + 1$
10. $b - \frac{4}{5} > \frac{3}{5}$
11. $8x - 3 < 2(1 - 12x)$

Exercise 2.5   Changing the subject of a formula

1. Volume of a cylinder .... $V = \pi r^2 h$
   Change the subject to h. Calculate h when $V = 33$ and $r = 2$.

2. A formula from Physics ...... $s = ut + \frac{1}{2}at^2$
   Change the subject to a. Calculate a when $s = 48$, $t = 3$ and $u = 4$.

3. Electric current in a circuit .. $I = \frac{V}{R}$
   Change the subject to R. Calculate R when $V = 240$ and $I = 15$.

4. Pythagoras' theorem .... $a^2 = b^2 + c^2$
   Change the subject to b. Calculate b when the hypotenuse is 17 and $c = 8$.

Exercise 2.6   Effect of changing one value in a formula

1. $A = \pi r^2$ If r is doubled, what is the effect on A?

2. $A = \frac{1}{2}bh$ If h is increased by 25%, what is the effect on A?

3. $I = \frac{C}{d^2}$ What is the effect on I if: **a.** C is increased by 10%?

   b. d is reduced by 50%?

Exercise 2.7   Quadratic equations

Solve: (Remember to look for **two solutions**, although they may be identical!)

1. $x^2 - 5x = 0$
   (common factor)
2. $2y^2 - 4y = 0$
3. $9 - 4a^2 = 0$
   (difference of squares)
4. $x^2 - 25 = 0$
5. $y^2 - 6y + 5 = 0$
6. $3t^2 - 10t + 3 = 0$
7. $2x^2 - 5x + 3 = 0$
8. $9y^2 - 12y + 4 = 0$
9. $6 + 5a - 6a^2 = 0$
10. $x^2 = 10x + 24$
    (first, arrange in standard quadratic form)
11. $y(y + 8) = 65$
12. $5t^2 - 30t + 45 = 0$
    (divide through by common factor 5 first)
13. $x^2 + (x - 1)^2 = 1$
14. $x^2 - 6x + 3 = 0$
    (use quadratic formula)
15. $5a^2 + 3a - 4 = 0$
16. $x^2 - 1\cdot7x - 1\cdot2 = 0$
17. $3t^2 = 12t - 11$
18. $1 - 2x - x^2 = 0$

See these pages in Leckie & Leckie's *Standard Grade Maths Revision Notes:*
page 10
page 10
page 12
page 12
page 13

3. Shape

Exercise 3.1 Angle and symmetry

See these pages in Leckie & Leckie's *Standard Grade Maths Revision Notes*:

page 14

page 15

page 15

1. Work out the angle sizes labelled *a* to *f*.

2. Write down the order of rotational symmetry.

a. 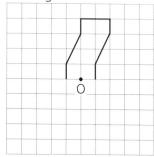   **b.** 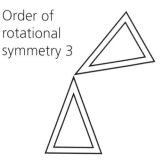   **c.**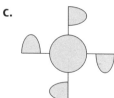

3. Complete the drawings:

a. Half turn symmetry about O

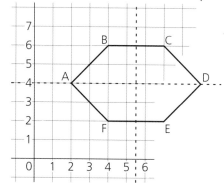

b. Order of rotational symmetry 3

4. Write down the coordinates of points A to F.

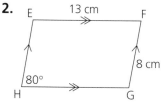

Exercise 3.2 Two-dimensional shapes

All the lines of symmetry have been drawn in with dashed lines on the shapes below. For each shape, give the name of the shape, the lengths of all its sides and the sizes of all its angles.

1.

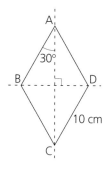

2.

E ——13 cm—— F

80°

8 cm

H ———— G

© Leckie & L

3.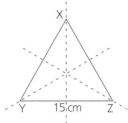

4.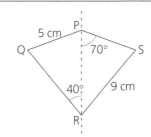

See these pages in Leckie & Leckie's *Standard Grade Maths Revision Notes:*

Exercise 3.3 Metric units

Practise changing metric measurements into different units:

page 14

	Measurement	change to		Measurement	change to
1.	350 mm	cm	**2.**	5·4 km	m
3.	750 ml	litres	**4.**	4000 cm³	litres
5.	46 cm	mm	**6.**	53 000 g	kg
7.	40 000 m	km	**8.**	2·9 tonnes	kg

Exercise 3.4 Area

page 16

Calculate the areas of these shapes.
　Remember **square** units. Remember too that the measurements must be in the same units before you do the calculation.

1. Rectangle, length 52 cm, breadth 31 cm

2. Square, side 4·8 m

3. Triangle, base 36 cm, height 25 cm

4. Rectangle, length 1 m 25 cm, breadth 80 cm (Answer in square metres.)

5. Triangle, base 1·4 cm, height 9 mm (Answer in square millimetres.)

6.

7.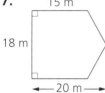

8.

9.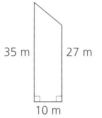

Exercise 3.5 Tolerance

page 16

Write down the upper and lower limits of these measurements:

1. (45 ± 0·1) cm　　　**2.** (4·6 ± 0·05) m　　　**3.** (60 ± 2)°

4. (450 ± 5) g　　　**5.** (27 ± 0·2) mm　　　**6.** (350 ± 1) ml

Exercise 3.6 Three-dimensional shapes

page 17

1. Here is the net of a solid shape. What is the shape?

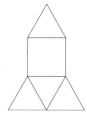

2. If all the sides in the diagram in question **1** represent 5 metres, what is the total length of the edges of the solid shape?

3. Shape

Exercise 3.7   Surface area and volume

Find the volume of each solid below.
It might be a good idea to find the cross-sectional area first. Give the volumes in cm³ or m³ and in litres.

1.   Cube

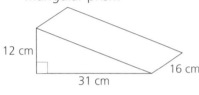

3 cm

2.   Cuboid

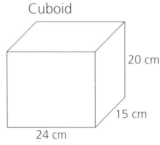

20 cm
15 cm
24 cm

3.   Cylinder

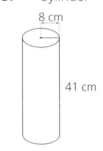

8 cm
41 cm

4.   Triangular prism

12 cm
31 cm
16 cm

5. Triangular prism

80 cm
2 m
1·3 m

6. Small cubes as in question **1** above are to be packed into the cuboid from question **2**.

    a. How many cubes will be needed to fill one layer in the cuboid?

    b. How many layers can be fitted in?

    c. What is the total volume of the cubes in the cuboid, in litres?

    d. Why does **6c** not have the same answer as question **2**, the volume of the cuboid?

7. The cuboid is to be packed in cardboard. No overlapping flaps will be needed as the edges will be taped over. What area of cardboard is required?

Exercise 3.8   Volumes and surface areas – composite solids

1. Calculate the volume.

33 cm
42 cm
30 cm

2. The volume is 128 000 cm³. Calculate the width.

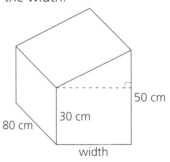

50 cm
80 cm
30 cm
width

3. Calculate the volume of water in the swimming pool.

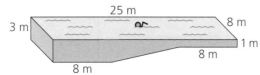

25 m
3 m
8 m
1 m
8 m
8 m

4. This 5-metre length of gutter holds 56·52 litres of rainwater when full. Find the diameter of the semi-circular cross-section.

See these pages in Leckie & Leckie's *Standard Grade Maths Revision Notes*:

pages 17–18, also page 45 for any shape involving a circle

pages 18–19

Exercise 4.1   Scientific notation

1. Write each of the following as a whole number or decimal:

a. $3{\cdot}5 \times 10^4$ **b.** 7×10^6 **c.** $4{\cdot}62 \times 10^2$

d. $2{\cdot}58 \times 10^5$ **e.** 3×10^{-3} **f.** $4{\cdot}6 \times 10^{-4}$

g. $1{\cdot}374 \times 10^{-2}$ **h.** $7{\cdot}54 \times 10^{-6}$ **i.** $4{\cdot}4 \times 10^0$

2. Write these in Scientific notation:

a. 5000   **b.** 83 000   **c.** 270 000

d. two million   **e.** 0·057   **f.** 0·0062

g. 0·0969   **h.** two tenths   **i.** 0·5

Exercise 4.2   Percentages

In this exercise, give answers to the nearest penny or whole number as appropriate.

Think carefully about whether you need to add or subtract the percentage amount.

1. Jacket in a sale, usual price, £49·99, discount 20%.

2. £34·50 shoes, discount 5%

3. £135 television, price increased by 3%

4. An increase of 12% in the number of pupils at a school, 920 before increase

5. 60 000 fish in a river, then 40% killed by pollution

6. Nurses' pay of £13 500 per annum, pay rise 3%

7. Garage bill of £218, with VAT at 17·5%

Exercise 4.3   Simple interest

Calculate

   a. the simple interest

   b. the final amount

   for each of these deposits.

The question tells you what the interest rate per annum is and how long the money is deposited.

1. £500   6%   1 year

2. £240   3%   2 years

3. £4500   2·5%   6 months

4. £12 000   4%   1 month

5. £660   4·5%   3 months

See these pages in Leckie & Leckie's *Standard Grade Maths Revision Notes*:

page 20

page 20

page 22

4. Arithmetic

Exercise 4.4   Time, distance and speed

See these pages in Leckie & Leckie's *Standard Grade Maths Revision Notes*:

1. Write these times in hours and minutes:

   a. 3·5 hours   b. 6·75 hours   c. 2·3 hours

page 21

2. Write these times as decimals of an hour:

   a. 4 hours 15 minutes   b. 7 hours 20 minutes   c. 1 hour 48 minutes
   (not 4·15!)

3. Given these departure times and journey times, find the arrival times:

   a. 0505   2 hours 15 minutes

   b. 1427   3 hours 45 minutes

   c. 2351   1 hour 30 minutes

   d. 0350   13 hours 40 minutes

4. For each of these journeys, work out the average speed, given the time taken and the distance travelled.
   Don't forget to write in the units!

   a. 3 hours, 180 miles   b. 4 hours, 258 km

   c. 2 hours 15 minutes, 162 km   d. 8 hours 18 minutes, 415 miles

5. Find D when S = 35 km/h and T = 3 hours 5 minutes.

6. Find D when S = 70 m/s and T = 2·4 s.

7. Find T when D = 350 miles and S = 70 mph.

8. Find T when D = 1925 km and S = 55 km/h.

Exercise 4.5   Percentage calculations

page 22

1. A restaurant bill including VAT at 17·5% is £62·04. Find the amount before VAT is added.

2. A doctor earns £51 205 after a 4·5% pay rise. What was the pay before the rise?

3. The price of a music system is reduced by 15% in a sale so it now costs £382·50. What did it cost before the sale?

Exercise 4.6   Compound interest and depreciation

page 23

1. Calculate the amount in a building society account after four years, where £5000 is deposited at 3% per annum.

2. Calculate what Scott's car is worth after 3 years if it cost £8600 new and depreciates at a rate of 12% each year.

   Did you manage to do these using powers, for example using 1·03^4 in question **1**? If so, well done, you'll have saved time. If not, don't worry – you'll learn all about it when you do Higher Mathematics!

Exercise 5.1 Graphs as pictures

Here is a graph showing how an athlete's heart rate varies on the racetrack.

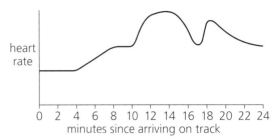

heart rate

minutes since arriving on track

The graph starts when the athlete arrives on the track. She takes part in two races, but first takes part in a warm-up jog. After 24 minutes outside altogether she returns indoors to the changing area.

1. When did she start the warm-up?

2. One race was a sprint but the other was longer. When did she begin the sprint?

3. Which race made her heart go faster?

4. Had her heart rate returned to normal when she left the track?

Exercise 5.2 Straight line graphs

1. The graph below shows the progress of a cruiser which leaves its marina and coasts at a steady speed until its engine fails, and of the rescue boat that goes to its aid.

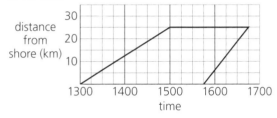

distance from shore (km)

time

a. The vessel left at 1300 hours. When did the engine fail?

b. How long did it take from the time the engine failed till the time the rescue boat set out?

c. How long did it take the rescue boat to arrive at the scene?

2. The graph on the right has a line representing the charges for visits to a swimming pool.

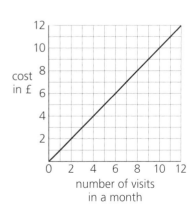

cost in £

number of visits in a month

a. It is possible to buy a membership card for £6 which gives 4 free visits per month. For each visit over 4, 50p entry fee must be paid. Draw a line on the graph to show the cost for up to 12 visits using the membership card.

b. For more than how many visits in a month would it be cheaper to buy a membership card?

c. What advice would you give to someone who was wondering if he or she should buy a membership card?

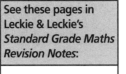

See these pages in Leckie & Leckie's *Standard Grade Maths Revision Notes:*

page 24

page 25

5. Graphs and Functions

3.

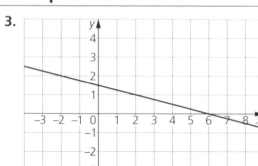

a. Write down the coordinates of the points where the line shown cuts the x- and y-axes.

b. Complete the table for the equation $y = 2x - 3$

x	0	1	2	3	4
y					

c. Draw this new line, $y = 2x - 3$, on the grid, using the values in the table.

d. Write down the point of intersection of the two lines.

 Exercise 5.3   Linear functions and graphs

1. For each line below write down:
   a. the gradient (m)   **b.** the y-intercept (0, c)   **c.** the equation

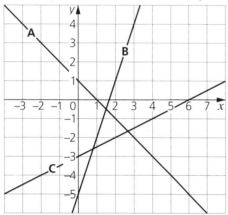

2. Draw these lines on a coordinate grid:
   a. $y = 2x - 5$ **b.** $y = -3x + 4$ **c.** $y = \frac{1}{2}x - 1$

3. Rearrange these equations of lines into $y = mx + c$ form:
   a. $2x - y = 5$ **b.** $4x + 2y + 9 = 0$ **c.** $3x + \frac{1}{2}y = 7$

 Exercise 5.4   Quadratic functions and function notation

1. The quadratic function, $f(x) = x^2 + 4x - 5$, is shown on the graph.

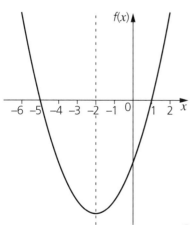

a. The graph cuts the x-axis at (–5, 0) and (1, 0). Factorise the quadratic to check these for yourself.

b. What is the equation of the axis of symmetry?

c. Where does the graph cut the y-axis? (Hint: evaluate $f(0)$.)

d. Find the minimum value of the function. (Hint: y-coordinate of the minimum turning point.)

2. $f(x) = x^2 + 3x + 1$ Calculate $f(0)$ and $f(3)$.

3. $g(x) = 2x^2 - 5$ Evaluate $g(-1)$.

4. $f(x) = -4x - 3$ Find the value of f when $x = 3$ and when $x = -2$.

See these pages in Leckie & Leckie's *Standard Grade Maths Revision Notes*:

page 25

page 26

Exercise 5.5   Simultaneous equations

Solve each pair of equations:

1. $x - y = 2$ and $2x + 3y = 4$

2. $x + y + 1 = 0$ and $x - 5y + 7 = 0$

3. $y = 2x + 3$ and $3x + 4y - 1 = 0$

4. $2x + 5y = 14$ and $3x - 2y = -17$

Exercise 5.6 $f(x) = a^x$ and $f(x) = \frac{a}{x}$

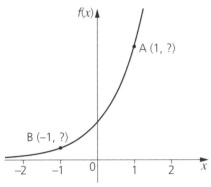

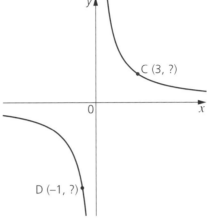

1. The first graph above is the exponential function, $f(x) = 3^x$. Write down the coordinates of the points A and B on the graph.

2. The second graph shows $y = \frac{6}{x}$. Write down the coordinates of C and D.

Exercise 5.7   Graphical solutions

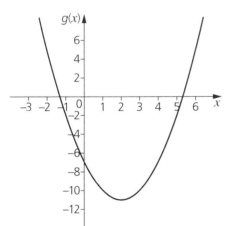

The graph shows the quadratic function $g(x) = x^2 - 4x - 7$. Answer from the graph:

1. How many solutions are there for the equation $x^2 - 4x - 7 = 2$?
(Hint: think of intersections with line $y = 2$.)

2. How many real solutions does $x^2 - 4x - 7 = -12$ have?

3. What value of k (approximately) gives only one solution for $x^2 - 4x - 7 = k$?

Exercise 5.8   Iteration

The quadratic function $g(x) = x^2 - 4x - 7$ in the previous exercise has one root between 5 and 6 and the other between -2 and -1. This can be seen on the graph.

Starting from $g(5) < 0$ and $g(6) > 0$, as can be seen on the graph, use an iterative method to find the solution, to two decimal places, which lies between 5 and 6. Find the other solution. You could use iteration again if you want the practice or you could use symmetry.

See these pages in
Leckie & Leckie's
*Standard Grade Maths
Revision Notes:*

page 26

pages 27
and 37

page 28

page 28

6. Maps, Plans and Similar Shapes

Exercise 6.1   Maps – scale

1. The real lengths and the scales are given. Work out the lengths on the maps.

	real lengths	scales
a.	85 m	1 cm represents 10 m
b.	2300 m	1 cm represents 500 m
c.	86 m	1:1000
d.	6 km	1:100 000

2. The lengths on the maps and the scales are given. Work out the real lengths.

	lengths on map	scales
a.	7·5 cm	1 cm represents 20 km
b.	9 mm	1 mm represents 40 m
c.	4·2 cm	1:10 000
d.	3·9 cm	1:10 000 000

3. Find the scales as representative fractions.

	lengths on map	real lengths
a.	5 cm	50 m
b.	4·2 cm	420 km
c.	25 mm	5 km
d.	5 cm	200 km

Exercise 6.2   Maps and scale drawings

Use the scale drawings to answer these questions:

1. Scale 1: 200 000

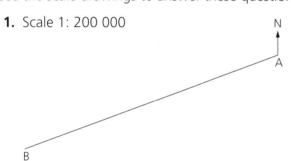

   A and B represent two villages.

   a. How far is it from A to B?
   b. What is the bearing of B from A?

2. Scale 1 cm represents 1 km.

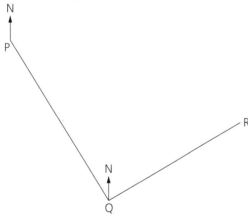

   A ship leaves P, sails to Q, then changes direction and sails to R.

   a. Give the distance and bearing from P to Q.
   b. Give the distance and bearing of R from Q.
   c. Give the distance and bearing of R from P.
   d. Once at R, a radio message tells the crew there is a stranded rowing boat 3 km away from them, but they don't hear the direction. Mark 5 possible positions on the diagram. Describe all the possible positions of the boat.

See these pages in Leckie & Leckie's *Standard Grade Maths Revision Notes*:

page 29

pages 30–32

Exercise 6.3   Similar shapes

1. These two right-angled triangles are **similar**.

Find the length of the side marked *h* cm.

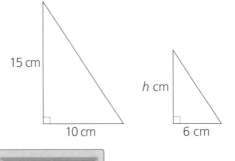

2. The screens of these monitors are mathematically **similar** shapes. The smaller screen has an area of 234 cm². Calculate the area of the larger screen.

Exercise 6.4   More similar shapes

1. Two parallel metal supports are keeping a vertical wall in position. Their lengths are marked on the diagram. The longer one reaches 2·5 metres up the wall. How far up does the shorter one reach?

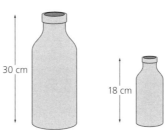

2. These triangles are similar. Find the values of *a* and *b*.

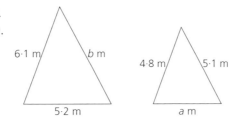

3. Find the length of AB.

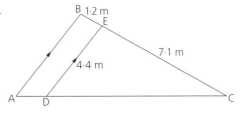

4. The bottles are mathematically similar. The volume of the smaller bottle is 500 ml. Find the volume of the larger bottle, to the nearest millilitre.

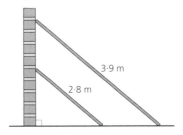

5. The packets of oats are mathematically similar. What weight of oats does the smaller pack hold?

See these pages in Leckie & Leckie's *Standard Grade Maths Revision Notes*:

pages 30–31

pages 32–33

7. Proportion and Variation

Exercise 7.1   Direct and inverse proportion

1. The supply of cornflakes at the scout camp was enough to last 20 scouts for 6 days. If 4 more scouts go to camp how many days will the cornflakes last?

2. A stack of 360 sheets of paper is 2·4 cm high. How high would a stack of 480 sheets be?

3. Walking at 4 km/h a group took 6 hrs 45 minutes to complete their day trek. At what speed would they have had to walk to complete it in 6 hours?

Exercise 7.2   Ratio

1. Simplify these ratios:
    a. 50p : £3   **b.** 1 hour : 35 minutes   **c.** 75 cm : 2 m

2. Split these quantities in the given ratios:
    a. £5 in the ratio 7 : 13   **b.** 1 litre in the ratio 3 : 1

Exercise 7.3   Pie charts

1. The pie chart shows the breakdown of different materials in a garment which weighs 120 g.

    Work out the weights of silk and cotton, to the nearest gram.

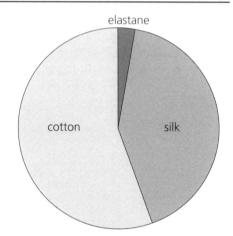

2. The pie chart shows how a catering company spent one year's budget.

    The wages bill was £31 000 000. Work out the total budget for the year and the transport costs, to the nearest million pounds.

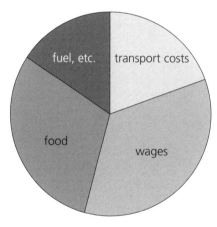

Exercise 7.4   Direct variation

1. V varies directly with *d* and when V is 3·6, *d* is 1·5. Find V when *d* = 5.

2. The force, P newtons, needed to pull a load varies directly with the weight, W newtons, of the load. When the load weighs 375 newtons, a force of 90 newtons is needed. Find P when W = 120.

3. Plot the following results of an electrical experiment on a graph and say how the graph shows that the voltage, V, varies directly with the current, I.

I	0·1	0·2	0·3	0·4	0·5	0·6
V	2	4	6	8	10	12

See these pages in Leckie & Leckie's *Standard Grade Maths Revision Notes*:

page 34

page 35

page 34

pages 35–36

Exercise 7.5   Inverse and joint variation

See these pages in
Leckie & Leckie's
*Standard Grade Maths
Revision Notes:*

pages 36–37
and page 12

1. The pressure P of a gas is inversely proportional to the volume V of the gas.

    When P = 400 N/m^2, V = 3 litres. Calculate V when P = 800 N/m^2.

2. Use the table of values below to explain why y varies inversely with x:

x	3	4	5	6
y	10	7·5	6	5

3. There is a law of variation connecting light intensity, I watts/m^2, with the distance, d cm, to the point being lit. It is known that I varies inversely with the square of d. Using the information on the graph and noting carefully the labels on the axes, find a formula connecting I and d. Use the formula to calculate I when d = 2 cm.

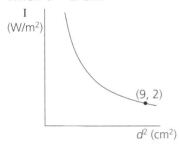

4. The weight, W g, of a bar varies directly as its length, L mm, and the square of its diameter, d mm. W = 240 g when d = 4 mm and L = 180 mm.

    a. Write a formula for W in terms of L and d.

    b. Calculate W when L = 150 mm and d = 8 mm.

5. The volume, V cm^3, of a given mass of gas varies directly as the temperature, T kelvins, and inversely as the pressure, P pascals. At a temperature of 360 kelvins and a pressure of 98 000 pascals, the volume of gas is 450 cm^3. At what temperature, to the nearest kelvin, is the gas when its volume is 300 cm^3 at a pressure of 128 000 pascals?

6. The gravitational force between two bodies varies inversely as the square of the distance between them. Venus is about twice as far from the Sun as Mercury. How will the force between Venus and the Sun compare with the force between Mercury and the Sun? (For this question, you may assume that Venus and Mercury have the same mass.)

7. A car's stopping distance varies directly as the speed squared and inversely as the resistance. Driver A is travelling at 40 km/h and driver B at 60 km/h. Driver A applies the brakes and comes to a halt after 20 metres.

    a. How many metres would the stopping distance for driver B be?

    b. In rain the resistance is halved. Find the stopping distances in rain for the two drivers.

8. Triangles and Trigonometry

Exercise 8.1   Theorem of Pythagoras

See these pages in
Leckie & Leckie's
*Standard Grade Maths
Revision Notes*:

pages 38 and
46

Round all answers to one decimal place.

1. A yacht sails East for 40 km then changes
course and sails South for 21 km, as
shown in the diagram. Calculate how far it
is from its starting point.

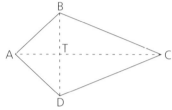

2. ABCD is a kite. AT = 5 cm, CT = 12 cm and
BD = 8 cm. Calculate the lengths AB and BC.

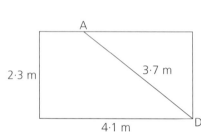

3. Kate has her computer at A in her room
(see floor plan). She has led a cable, length
3·7 m, from the telephone socket at the
corner, D, of the room to the computer so
that she can access the Internet. Her father
says that this cable trailing over the floor is
dangerous and insists that she must get a
longer one which can be led around the wall
to the computer. How long does she need
the new cable to be?

4. On a coordinate grid, plot the points P(–2, 3) and Q(2, –5). Use Pythagoras'
Theorem to find the length of the line PQ.

Exercise 8.2   Trigonometry in right-angled triangles

page 38

1. A mast 10 metres tall has 13 metres long
cables to keep it in position. Only one cable
is shown in the diagram. Calculate the angle
marked x in the diagram.

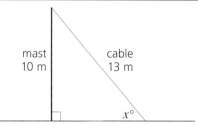

2. Town B is 13 km from town A on a bearing
of 022°. How far North is B from A?
(Distance marked ? on diagram).

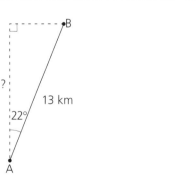

3. The diagram shows a sloping ramp. Calculate
the height.
(Height is marked H on the diagram).

Exercise 8.3 More trigonometry in right-angled triangles

See these pages in
Leckie & Leckie's
*Standard Grade Maths
Revision Notes:*

pages 39
and 42

1. Two windsurfers, A and B, can be seen from the top, C, of a 42 metre high cliff. The windsurfers are in a straight line from P. The angle of depression of A from the top of the cliff is 38° (marked on the diagram) and the angle of depression of B is 52°. Find the distance between the windsurfers, AB.
   (Hint: find PA and PB first.)

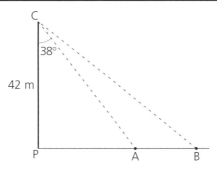

2. A ramp has been placed to allow access to a raised platform. Calculate the length of the ramp from top to bottom, to one decimal place.

3. A spotlight positioned at floor level at the front of the stage is to be directed at a point on the backcloth, 2·7 metres above floor level. The spotlight is set for an angle of elevation of 23°. Will the beam of light hit the desired point, or will it be too high or too low? Explain your answer by including some calculations.

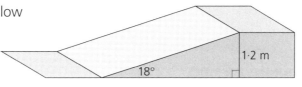

Exercise 8.4 Trigonometric equations

page 40

Solve these equations for $0 \leqslant x < 360$, remembering that there will usually be two solutions. Give your answers correct to one decimal place.

1. $\sin x° = 0·76$ 2. $\cos x° = 0·56$ 3. $\tan x° = 4·3$

4. $\sin x° = -0·8$ 5. $\cos x° = -0·14$ 6. $\tan x° = -9·5$

7. $5 \sin x° - 2 = 1$ 8. $3 \tan x° + 4 = 10$ 9. $2 \cos x° + 3 = 2·2$

Exercise 8.5 Sine rule, cosine rule, and formula for area of a triangle

page 41

Draw sketches for questions 1–4 to help you find the missing quantities. Round your answers to three significant figures.

Remember the notation: 'a' means the side opposite angle A. (Angle A can be written as Â.)

1. Triangle ABE, $a = 25$, $Â = 100°$, $Ê = 28°$. Find e.

2. Triangle GHJ, $g = 2$, $h = 5$, $Ĵ = 65°$. Find the length of the third side.

3. Triangle TUV, $t = 6$, $u = 7$, $v = 5$. Calculate the size of $Û$.

4. Triangle ABC, $b = 8·2$, $c = 12·5$, $Â = 123°$. Find the area.

5. The sketch shows the position of three holes on a golf course. The distance AB is 610 metres, AC is 515 metres and angle BCA is 53°. Find the size of the acute angle ABC.

6. A mountain road from a point P to the summit is 1·6 km long and makes an angle of 5° with the horizon. It descends on the other side to a point Q on the same level as P, making an angle of 7° with the horizon. What would be the length of a straight tunnel from P to Q?

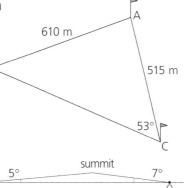

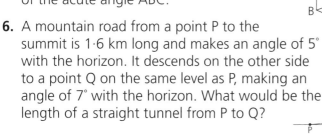

8. Triangles and Trigonometry

7. A ship sails 115 km due East from port P to port Q. Then it changes direction and sails 95 km on a bearing of 198° to port R.

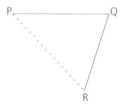

See these pages in Leckie & Leckie's *Standard Grade Maths Revision Notes:*

   a. Find the distance from P to R.

   b. Calculate the bearing the ship must take to return to P.

8. **a.** Calculate the area of this gable end wall.

   b. If paint coverage is 8 square metres per litre, how much paint will be needed to paint the wall?

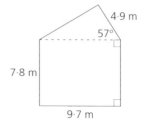

Exercise 8.6 Trigonometric graphs

pages 42–44

1. The diagram shows two graphs. One is of the function $y = \cos x°$. What is the other?

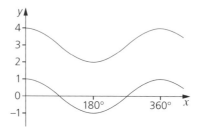

2. The diagram shows the graph of $y = a \sin bx°$, $0 \leqslant x < 360$. Find the values of a and b.

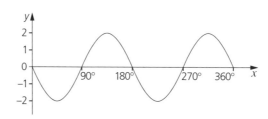

3. The diagram shows the graph of $y = k \cos cx°$, $0 \leqslant x < 720$. Find the values of k and c.

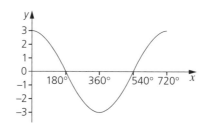

4. What are the maximum and minimum values of the function $f(x) = \sin x° - 4$?

5. What is the period of the function $y = 2 \cos 2x°$?

6. The number of hours of daylight, H, at different times of the year in some parts of central Scotland is approximated by the formula
H = 12 + 5 sin (30M − 80)° where M is the number of months since 1st January.

   a. How many hours of daylight are there on 1 July (that is, when M = 6)?

   b. What is the maximum and minimum number of daylight hours? (Think of the graph.)

   c. What is the value of M for the longest day?
(This is the day with the maximum number of daylight hours.
sin (30 − M)° is maximum for what value of the angle?)

   d. Sunrise is at 8·23 am on 1st November. Work out the approximate time of sunset on this day.
(Start by evaluating H using the appropriate value of M.)

   e. Find the two values of M for which H = 12.

Exercise 9.1   Circumference and area

1. Calculate the area and the circumference, C, correct to three significant figures, of circles with the following diameters:

   a. 4 cm   **b.** 45 m   **c.** 2·36 m

2. C = 57 cm, calculate d, the diameter.

3. C = 614 m, calculate r, the radius.

4. In parts **a** and **b** below, find the circumference. In **c** find the radius.

   a.  22 cm
   b.  13 mm
   c. 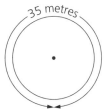 35 metres

5. Find the perimeter:

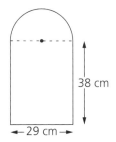
38 cm   29 cm

6. Find the area:

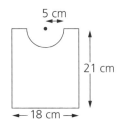
5 cm   21 cm   18 cm

Exercise 9.2   Angles and tangents

MP, NP and RT are tangents to their circles.

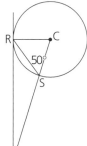
M O 150° N P

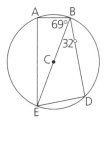
R C 50° S T

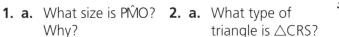
A B 69° 32° C E D

1. **a.** What size is PM̂O? Why?
   b. Find MP̂N.

2. **a.** What type of triangle is △CRS?
   b. What size is RĈS?
   c. Find RT̂C.

3. **a.** Why is EÂB = 90°?
   b. Name another right angle in the diagram.
   c. Work out the size of AÊD.

Exercise 9.3   Arcs, sectors and chords

See these pages in
Leckie & Leckie's
*Standard Grade Maths
Revision Notes:*

pages 46–47

Give all answers to three significant figures.

1. Find the shaded area:

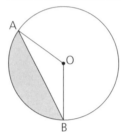

3 cm

3 cm

2. Find the shaded area:

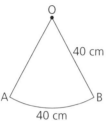

A   O   B

AÔB = 125°
AO = 4·5 cm
AB = 8 cm
(Hint: first find area of
sector AOB. Then find
area of △AOB.)

3. Find the length of the (minor) arc AB.

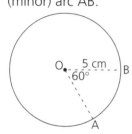

O 5 cm B
60°
A

4. Find the size of AÔB.

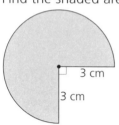

O

40 cm

A   B
40 cm

5. Find ST.

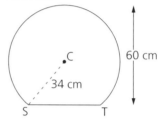

C
34 cm
60 cm
S   T

6. Find the perimeter.

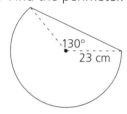

130°
23 cm

You will need these sets of data in the following exercises:

See these pages in Leckie & Leckie's *Standard Grade Maths Revision Notes:*

A Number of jelly babies in 20 randomly selected packets

39	34	39	41	37	36	40	38	36	36
38	37	40	39	33	36	35	36	40	38

B Monthly rainfall figures, in millimetres, for a certain Scottish resort

Jan	Feb	Mar	Apr	May	Jun	Jul	Aug	Sep	Oct	Nov	Dec
150	140	125	134	110	85	56	32	47	77	102	123

C Number of videos hired each day from a video rental shop

45	57	78	48	56	82	88	49	69	46	75	61
45	83	32	79	70	47	53	66	38	91	74	53

D
age (years)	11	11·5	11·5	12	12·5	13	13	13·5	14
height (cm)	140	140	145	145	165	145	150	150	155

(continued)	14·5	15	15	15·5	16	16	16·5	17	17
	145	142	160	155	169	152	163	163	170

Exercise 10.1 Frequency table, bar chart, line graph, stem and leaf chart

1. For data set **A** make a frequency table and draw a bar graph.

page 48

2. For data set **B** draw a line graph.

3. For data set **C** construct a stem and leaf chart.

page 50

4. The back-to-back stem and leaf chart below shows the heights of a class when they were in first year and the same pupils' heights when they were in second year.

page 50

```
class 1A  1999        class 2A  2000
              8 | 12 | 8
    7  4  2  1 | 13 | 1  2  9
 8  8  3  2  2 | 14 | 4  5  7  7  8  9
    9  7  3  2 | 15 | 1  2  2  2
    6  4  4  3 | 16 | 3  5  5  6
              1 | 17 | 0  1

n = 20                n = 20
    15 | 2 represents 152 cm
```

a. Work out the median for first year and second year. Comment on your results.

b. Work out the range for first and second year. Comment on your results.

5. The line graph shows the average house price in January of each year over a decade in a region of Scotland.

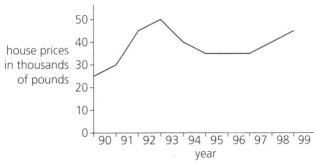

a. Estimate the average house price for 1995.

b. In what years were prices highest? Estimate the highest price.

c. During which years did house prices fall?

d. Describe briefly the trend in house prices over the decade.

10. Statistics

Exercise 10.2 Mean, mode, median, range and probability

See these pages in Leckie & Leckie's *Standard Grade Maths Revision Notes*:

1. For data sets **A**, **B** and **C** (on page 25), calculate:

   a. the mean   b. the median

   c. the range   d. the mode (data set **A** only)

pages 48–49

2. The mean of five children's ages is 8·4 years. Four of the children's ages are 10, 9, 4 and 8. What age is the fifth child?

3. Write the probabilities of these events, as fractions:

   a. Throwing a six with one throw of a die.

   b. Picking an even number from those on a clock face.

   c. Picking a red sock out of a bag containing 4 red and 6 black socks.

   d. Choosing a letter at random from the word **MISSISSIPPI** and it being an '**S**'.

Exercise 10.3 Scattergraphs

page 50

1.

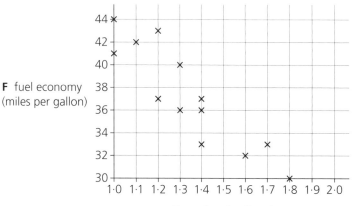

F fuel economy (miles per gallon) vs **E** engine size (litres)

   a. How many miles do you get to the gallon with the car with the 1·6 litre engine?

   b. What engine size gave the best fuel economy? ('Best' means used the least fuel.)

   c. Describe the correlation between engine size and fuel economy.

   d. Draw a line of best fit on the diagram.

   e. Use the line of best fit to find what fuel economy you would expect for a car with a 1·5 litre engine.

2. Draw a scattergraph for data set **D** (on page 25). Draw the best-fitting line. Describe the correlation.

Exercise 10.4 Cumulative frequency and quartiles

pages 52–53

1. a. Add a cumulative frequency column to the frequency table you drew for Exercise 10.1, Question **1**.

   b. Calculate the upper and lower quartiles for the data.

   c. Calculate the semi-interquartile range for the data.

2. Calculate the upper and lower quartiles and the semi-interquartile range for data set **C**.

Exercise 10.5 Box plots, dot plots and pie charts

1. Construct a dot plot for data set **A**.

2. The box plot shows the attendances at a weekly after-school revision class for Standard Grade Maths. The class ran for 20 weeks.

   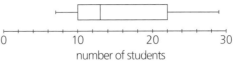

   number of students

   a. Complete these statements:
   The median attendance was ...... students.
   The lowest attendance was ..... students.
   The range of the attendance was ....
   The upper quartile for the data is ......

   b. There are supposed to be at least 10 students for a session to run. How many times should the class have been cancelled?

   c. Was the attendance usually more or less than 15 students per session?

3. Construct a box plot for data set **A**.

4. Draw a pie chart to show this breakdown of sales of yoghurt in a grocery:
   plain 35   strawberry 57   vanilla 24   peach 49   blackberry 15

Exercise 10.6 Scattergraph – equation of best-fitting line

1. Look at the scattergraph in Exercise 10.3, question **1**. One good line of best fit (not the only one) is the line passing through (1·0, 44) and (1·6, 32). The equation of the line is $F = aE + b$ for two numbers a and b.
   Find a and b and write down the equation of this line.

2. The scattergraph for Exercise 10.3 question **2** (using data set **D**) has a possible best-fitting line passing through (11, 140) and (13·5, 150).
   (You can see this graph and line in the answers for Exercise 10.3.)

   The equation of the line is $H = pA + q$
   Find p and q and write down the equation of the line.

Exercise 10.7 Standard deviation

1. The number of sightings of foxes in a city park was recorded over seven weeks.

   Here is the data: 61 34 12 23 8 18 26

   Calculate: **a** the mean and **b** the standard deviation of this data.

2. The amounts of pocket money given to 10 seven-year-olds are listed.

   £1·50 75p 90p £1·20 £1·70 50p £1 £1·25 90p £1·00

   Calculate **a** the mean and **b** the standard deviation for the sample (to the nearest whole number of pence).

3. A sample of ten men in their twenties was timed running a mile to judge the fitness of this age group. The times were recorded in minutes.

   Results: $\sum x = 75$ $\sum x^2 = 606$

   a. Calculate the mean and standard deviation of this data.

   b. A group of men in their fifties was then timed over the same course in order to compare the fitness of older and younger men. This sample had a mean of 10·3 minutes and a standard deviation of 5·1. What does this say about the fitness of the two age groups?

See these pages in Leckie & Leckie's *Standard Grade Maths Revision Notes*:

page 52

page 53

page 51

pages 54–55

General Exam A   Paper 1

Time   35 minutes
Calculators not allowed

1. **a.** $3·5 - 6 + 8·1$
    b. $14·6 ÷ 20$
    c. 40% of 635 kg
    d. $36 × 45$

2. Kevin spends $\frac{1}{4}$ of his pocket money on sweets and snacks, $\frac{3}{8}$ on entertainment, $\frac{1}{8}$ on fares and saves the rest. His pocket money is £10.
    a. How much does he spend on entertainment?
    b. What fraction does he save?

3. The 3-digit code for Shona's sports locker is a multiple of both 5 and 3, and is made up of only even numbers.
    a. Write down 4 possibilities for the code.
    b. If the middle digit is a prime number, what is the code?

4. The number of sheets on a toilet roll of a certain brand is $280 ± 8$. What is the largest number of sheets you can expect altogether in a 4-pack of this brand?

5. The minimum temperatures over seven successive nights in Orkney were

    $7°$ $9°$ $6°$ $-1°$ $-3°$ $-4°$ $0°$

    What was the mean minimum temperature over the week?

6. The table shows microwave cooking times for different amounts of the same food:

Mass (M)	Time (T)
100 g	2 minutes
150 g	3 minutes
200 g	4 minutes
250 g	5 minutes
300 g	?
......	
1000 g	?
.....	
4000 g	?

    a. There is a simple rule connecting T and M. Fill in the blanks in the table.
    b. Complete the formula for cooking time:
    $T = \ldots$

7. The number of guests staying overnight at a small hotel over a two-week period was recorded, as shown here:

Day	week 1	week 2
Mon	12	13
Tues	25	14
Wed	49	39
Thur	16	10
Fri	56	62
Sat	46	58
Sun	21	29

    a. Construct a 2-digit back-to-back stem and leaf chart to show this information, where, for example, 3 | 6 represents 36 guests.
    b. To encourage people to come to the hotel midweek there is a bargain rate one night. Write down which night it is and explain how you know.

8. The diagram shows the radar screen at air traffic control at Dyce airport. D stands for Dyce which is shown at the centre of the diagram. The rings on the screen have radii 100 km, 200 km, 300 km, etc. A represents an aircraft approaching the airport.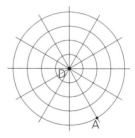
    a. Make a scale drawing showing D and A, using the scale 1:10 000 000.
    b. Another aircraft is at B which is 800 km due East of A. Mark the position of B on your diagram.
    c. Use your scale drawing to give the distance and bearing of B from D.

General Exam A   Paper 2

Time   55 minutes
Calculators allowed

1. In 1976 the population of India was 564 218 000. Write this figure in Scientific notation.

2. Mrs Scott bought a camcorder for £245 to take on the family holiday to Greece. While in Greece she spotted the same camcorder priced at 109 505 drachmae. The exchange rate is 523·8 drachmae to the pound. Would it have been cheaper for her to buy the camcorder in Greece? Explain your answer.

3. The number of hours of sunshine each day for a month is recorded in a frequency table.

Hours of sunshine	Frequency	Hours × Frequency
0	3	
1	7	
2	4	
3	9	
4	3	
5	5	

  a. Complete the table and calculate the mean, in hours, correct to two decimal places.

  b. What is the range of the distribution?

4. The distance table gives the distances in km between various places in Scotland.

Aberdeen

95	Braemar				
266	201	Fort William			
169	121	106	Inverness		
135	256	127	135	Kyle of Lochalsh	
373	325	314	208	304	John o' Groats

Greg drives from Braemar to Inverness to see a client, then on to John o' Groats for a meeting. He stays overnight then drives to Fort William the next day, where he stays for several days before driving back to Braemar.

  a. What distance has he driven altogether?

  b. His firm gives him 36 pence per kilometre travelling expenses. Calculate his travelling expenses for the complete trip.

5. Ken, Helen and Rory took part in a sponsored swim for charity. Helen raised £8 more than Rory and Ken raised £5 more than Rory. Between them they raised £79.

  a. Form an equation using the information you have been given.

  b. Solve the equation to find how much Ken raised.

6. On a coordinate grid plot the points P(1, 2), Q(−3, −1), and R(1, −8).

  a. Plot the point S so that PQRS is a kite.

  b. Calculate the gradient of the line PQ.

  c. Calculate the area of the triangle PQR.

7. Circular lids for cans are cut, according to the following diagram, from a rectangular piece of aluminium measuring 98 cm by 30 cm. The radius of each lid is 7 cm.

  a. Work out how many complete lids can be cut. (A rough sketch may help.)

  b. Calculate, to the nearest cm^2, the area of aluminium that is wasted.

8. The angle of elevation of the top of a tower is measured from a point 30 metres away from the base of the tower. The angle of elevation is 52°. Draw a rough sketch and use it to help you calculate the height of the tower to one decimal place.

9. The formula to find the volume of a cone is $V = \frac{1}{3}\pi r^2 h$, where r is the base radius and h is the height.

  a. A cone modelled from clay has dimensions $r = 8$ cm and $h = 20$ cm. Find V to the nearest cm^3.

  b. Is there enough clay in the cone to make a cube of side 12 cm? You must give reasons for your answer.

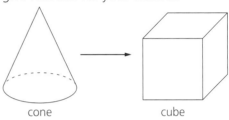

cone   cube

10. At the school fair, coloured balloons, each with a number for the prize draw, are released. There are 60 red balloons, 40 white and 20 green. If you were to catch a balloon, what is the probability of its being white? (Give your answer as a fraction in its lowest terms.)

11. Carol invests £9500 in a building society account which gives 4·5% per annum. After 4 months she withdraws her money to pay for building a conservatory. How much interest does she receive?

12. A kite has sides of 18 cm and 35 cm, and the shorter diagonal is 28 cm, as shown in the diagram. Find the length of the longer diagonal.

18 cm

28 cm

35 cm

13. A school starts the year with 964 pupils. At the end of May, 134 pupils in S4–6 are going to leave, and there are 229 applications from pupils to join S1 the following August.

  a. What is the expected percentage rise in the school roll?

  b. The local authority has promised a building expansion programme when the roll exceeds 1000. Will the school reach that level in August? Give a reason.

  c. The pupil/teacher ratio is 20 to 1. How many extra teachers (rounded up to a whole number) should be employed in August?

General Practice Exam B

General Exam B   Paper 1

Time   35 minutes
Calculators not allowed

1. a. 22·1 − 6·84
   b. 30% of 23·5 kg
   c. 49·6 ÷ 20
   d. 6 × (−7)

2. The temperature was 5°C at 6 pm but fell by 8° overnight. What was the temperature overnight?

3. A school is planning a day of sponsored activities. Pupils can choose a sponsored walk, sponsored readathon, or opt out altogether. There are 640 pupils in the school. $\frac{3}{5}$ opt for the sponsored walk and $\frac{1}{4}$ for the sponsored readathon.
   a. How many pupils chose the sponsored walk?
   b. What fraction of the pupils opted out?

4. In the diagram, AB is a diameter of the circle with centre O. BC is a tangent to the circle at B. Angle BOC = 67°. BD and OC are parallel. Write down the size of these angles:
   a. Angle DBA
   b. Angle DAB
   c. Angle BCO.

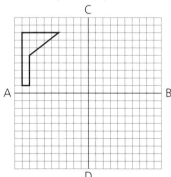

5. a. Factorise $3x - 6xy$
   b. Solve the equation $7x + 2 = 3x + 10$

6. Complete the diagram so that AB and CD are both lines of symmetry.

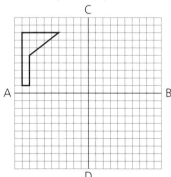

7. A microbe measures 2.56×10^{-5} m. Write this number in full.

8. The pie chart shows how the sixth year, which had 48 pupils, voted in the election for head girl.

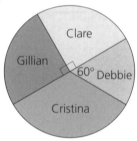

How many pupils voted for Cristina?

General Exam B   Paper 2

Time   55 minutes
Calculators allowed

1. Write down the mode of this data set.

3	9	4	6	4	8	3	8
7	4	4	5	4	7	6	8
3	4	9	4	6	7	4	2

2. The two photo clip frames shown here are similar in shape.
The area of the smaller frame is 140 cm². Calculate the area of the larger frame.

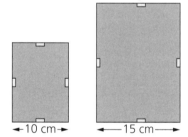

3. A recipe for scones uses flour and butter in the ratio 4 to 1. Scott is going to make as many scones as he can from the bag of flour in his parents' kitchen. When he weighs the flour he finds he has 560 g. There is plenty of butter in the fridge.
   a. How much butter should he use to go with 560 g of flour?
   b. 200 g of flour (along with the other ingredients) makes a batch of 15 scones. How many scones should Scott be able to make?

4. A digital TV can be bought on hire purchase by paying a deposit of £55 and 18 monthly payments of £27·85.
   a. What is the total hire purchase price of the TV?
   b. The same TV can be bought for a cash price of £490. Express the extra paid on hire purchase as a percentage of the cash price.

5. Ken hires out equipment for home improvements. He buys a second-hand floor sander for £346·70 and spends a further £57 restoring it to good condition.
He hires it out at £18 per day.
How many days hire will be needed before he has recovered his full costs?

6. Find the gradient of the section of road shown below.

7. A large figure of eight is painted on the side of a shed.
The radius of the smaller circle is 68 cm.
The height of the figure is 3·2 metres.
   a. Find the diameter of the larger circle.
   b. Calculate the total length of the line of paint tracing out the figure of eight.

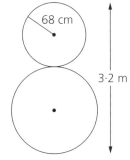

8. The diagram shows an isosceles triangle of base 4 cm and height 2·8 cm.
Calculate the size of the equal angles indicated in the diagram.

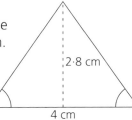

9. Part of a straight line graph is shown below.

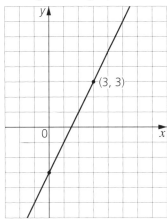

   a. Complete the table to show the coordinates of some points on the line.

x	0	1	2	3	4	5
y				3		

   b. Write down a formula for finding y when you know x.
   c. The point $(-5, n)$ lies on the line. Find n.

10. The operation # means 'double the first number and add the result to the square of the second number'.
For example, $4 \# 3 = 2 \times 4 + 3^2$
$= 8 + 9 = 17$.
   a. Evaluate $5 \# 4$.
   b. If $7 \# a = 15$ and a is positive, find a.

11. The braking distance, D metres, of a train varies directly as the square of its speed, V km/h.
The braking distance is 160 metres when the train is travelling at 80 km/h.
Calculate the braking distance when the train's speed is 120 km/h.

12. Calculate the area of the rhombus shown below.

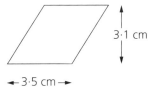

13. Kirsty sells insurance policies. Her monthly salary is £400 plus 2% commission on all her sales of insurance policies in that month.
In January her total pay is £832.
What value of policies did she sell in January?

Credit Exam A   Paper 1

Time   **55 minutes**
Calculators not allowed

1. Evaluate:
   a. $25 + 22 \cdot 5 \div 3$
   b. $\frac{3}{5}$ of $(\frac{1}{2} + \frac{1}{3})$

2. Evaluate these expressions where $p = -3$, $q = 4$ and $r = 0$:
   a. $pq - q^2$
   b. $3p + \frac{r}{q}$

3. Simplify $(2x + 5y)(3x - 5y)$

4. Solve algebraically:
   a. $8x^2 - 10x - 3 = 0$
   b. $\frac{x}{(8 + x)} = 9$

5. T varies directly with the square of W and inversely with X. For particular values of W and X, T is 24. If W is unchanged but X is doubled, what is the value of T?

6. $f(x) = x^2 + \frac{1}{x}$ Find $f(4)$.

7. Express $\sqrt{50}$ as a surd in its simplest form.

8. Express in simplest form: $\frac{2a^3}{4a^5}$

9. a. Factorise $x^2 - 9$.
   b. Express in its simplest form: $\frac{x^2 - 9}{2x + 6}$

10. The jugs in the picture are mathematically similar.

10 cm   20 cm

The volume of the smaller jug is 0·4 litres. Find the volume of the larger jug.

Credit Exam A   Paper 2

Time   **80 minutes**
Calculators allowed

1. The number of minutes Becky spent surfing the net was recorded each evening for a fortnight. Here are the results:

week 1	week 2
25	13
14	16
18	20
43	37
34	27
46	52
75	63

   a. Calculate the median and upper and lower quartiles.
   b. Show the information as a box plot.

2. $E = mc^2$ is an important formula in physics. Calculate E if $m = 8 \times 10^{-3}$ kg and $c = 3 \times 10^8$ m/s.

3. If a polygon has s sides, the number of diagonals, d, can be worked out from the formula: $d = \frac{s^2 - 3s}{2}$
   a. Find the number of diagonals for a decagon (10 sides).
   b. There is a polygon which has twice as many diagonals as sides. What is s for this polygon?
   c. Some polygons have more sides than diagonals. Find **all** of these.
      (Hint: First solve the equation for when d equals s.)

4. A ship is sailing on a bearing of 052° and will soon sail past a lighthouse. The lighthouse is 6 km away on a bearing of 063° (see sketch). It is not permitted for a vessel to sail within 1 km of the lighthouse.

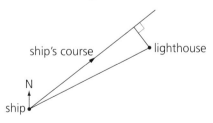

Can the ship continue on its present course? You must justify your answer.

5. An observatory has a hemispherical dome of radius 4 metres on the roof, as shown in the diagram. The main part of the building is a cube of side 9 metres. All the exposed surfaces are to be painted.

   a. The formula for the surface area of a sphere is A = 4πr². Find the area of the hemisphere. (Disregard the telescope and the gap it projects through.)
   b. Find the area of the flat part of the roof.
   c. Calculate the total area to be painted, to the nearest square metre.

6. Luke bought his first flat five years ago and is now selling it. He discovers that its value has increased by 18% during the five years. It is now valued at £45 000. What did he pay for his flat five years ago? Give your answer to the nearest thousand pounds.

7. The wind speed (in knots) recorded at the Cairngorm weather station each day for a week is as follows:

   16   2   7   0   11   18   2

   a. Calculate the mean and range.
   b. Calculate the standard deviation.

8. The diagram shows a circle inside an isosceles triangle. The sides of the triangle are tangents to the circle. One angle of the triangle is 40°. Calculate the size of the angle marked a°.

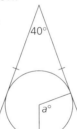

9. The air drag on a car varies with S, the surface area of the car, and with the square of V, the speed of the car. If the car increases speed from 40 km/h to 120 km/h, what will be the effect on the air drag?

10. Two observers are watching a hot air balloon. One is at the top of a 200 metre high tower and observes the balloon at an angle of elevation of 20°. The other is at the foot of the tower and observes the balloon at an angle of elevation of 47°.

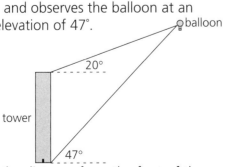

Calculate the distance from the foot of the tower to the balloon.

11. Jenna wants to hire a mobile phone. 'Dialup' has a fixed charge of £20 per month and gives 30 minutes of call time free with the rest charged at 40 pence a minute.
   a. What is Jenna's bill for a month in which her total call time is 80 minutes?
   b. Write down a formula for the total cost, £C, for Jenna's phone in a month where her total call time is t minutes, where t ⩾ 30.

Jenna investigates another mobile phone company, 'Chataway'. Its fixed charge is £18 per month and all calls are charged at 35 pence a minute.
   c. Write down a formula for the cost, £C, for a month where the total call time is t minutes.
   d. Use the two formulae to find the number of minutes of call time in a month which will cost the same with either company.

12. a. The diagram shows the graph of y = k cos ax°, 0 ⩽ x < 180.

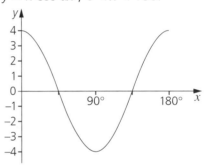

   Find the values of a and k.
   b. Solve algebraically the equation 3 tan x° + 7 = 0 for 0 ⩽ x < 360.

Credit Practice Exam B

Credit Exam B   Paper 1

Time   55 minutes
Calculators not allowed

1. Evaluate:
   a. $8\frac{2}{5} \div 1\frac{1}{5}$
   b. $-6 \cdot 7 + 3 \cdot 2 \times 1 \cdot 5$

2. Evaluate these expressions where $x = 7$, $y = -2$, and $z = 3$.
   a. $x^2 y$
   b. $\frac{x}{z} + yz$

3. Simplify
   a. $2\sqrt{5} - 6\sqrt{5}$
   b. $\frac{x^5}{x^{-2}}$

4. Find a relationship connecting x and y, using the information given in the diagram.

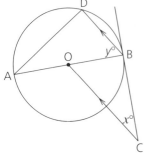

5. If $\sin x^\circ = \frac{1}{\sqrt{3}}$ and $\cos x^\circ = \frac{2\sqrt{2}}{\sqrt{3}}$, find the exact value of $\tan x^\circ$, giving your answer with a rational denominator.
   (Hint: use a trig identity.)

6. a. Factorise $a^2 b - a^3 b^2$
   b. Solve algebraically $2x - \frac{4}{x} = 7$

7. a. If $f(x) = 3x^2$, find the value of $f(a^2)$.
   b. Express in simplest form $\frac{3x^2 + x - 10}{2x + 4}$

8. $F = 6 + \frac{5}{M}$
   Change the subject of the formula to M.

9. Give the median and the semi-interquartile range of the data represented in the box plot.

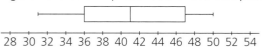

28 30 32 34 36 38 40 42 44 46 48 50 52 54

Credit Exam B   Paper 2

Time   80 minutes
Calculators allowed

1. The number of bacteria on a slide is increasing by 15% every hour. At 6 am there are 2 000 000 bacteria. How many are there at 9 am? Give your answer in Scientific notation correct to 2 significant figures.

2. The ages of a group of girls taking part in a dance show are shown in the table below:

Age	Number of girls	Cumulative frequency
5	2	
6	1	
7	3	
8	4	
9	4	
10	6	
11	8	
12	19	
13	3	
14	1	
15	1	

   a. Complete the cumulative frequency column.
   b. The local paper wants to take a group photo of the ten youngest girls. Up to what age of girl will be selected for the photo?

3. Solve algebraically the inequality
   $12 - (y + 5) < 3$

4. The plug is pulled out of a bath containing 220 litres of water. The bath empties at a steady rate. After 40 seconds it is empty.

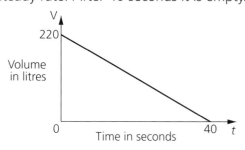

   Find the equation of the straight line in terms of V and t.

5. A tennis ball is lobbed over the net by a player standing 5 metres behind the net. The path of the ball is in the shape of a parabola with equation $h(x) = 1 + 0.8x - 0.08x^2$ where $h(x)$ gives the height of the ball above the ground when it has travelled x metres horizontally from the player's racket.

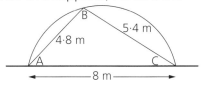

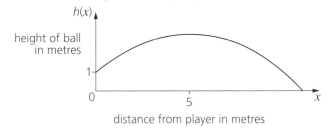

a. What is the height of the ball when it crosses the net?

b. What is the distance from the player's racket when the ball is again 1 metre above the ground?

6. The number of visits made to the doctor in a year by a sample of 20 elderly patients is shown below.

2	6	4	3	8
5	1	0	2	0
4	5	2	0	10
4	1	2	9	8

Show this information on a dot plot. State the modal number of visits.

7. The two triangles in the diagram are similar. Calculate the length of EF.

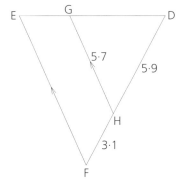

8. Solve the equation $x^2 - 3x - 8 = 0$, giving your answers correct to 1 decimal place.

9. An open shed to cover sacks of grain has a segment of a circle for its cross-section. The roof has two supports, AB and BC.

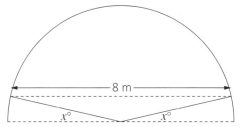

a. Use the dimensions in the diagram to prove that the cross-section is not a semicircle.

b. The radius of the circle of which the cross-section is a segment is 4·1 metres. Use the sketch below to find the size of the angle marked $x°$.

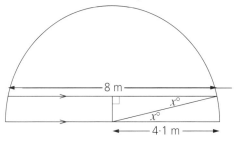

c. Find the length of the arc which forms the shed's cross-section.

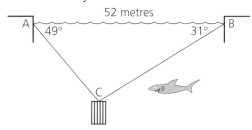

10. A steel cage for observing sharks is held underwater by two cables.

The cables are secured at sea level, 52 metres apart (points A and B on diagram). Also marked on the diagram are the angles of depression of the cage from points A and B. What depth underwater is the point C?

11. A car travels on a journey of 500 km at an average speed of x km/hour.

a. Write an expression using x for the time taken to complete the journey.

b. Over the same period of time a second car travels at 30 km/hour. Write an expression involving x for the distance the second car will complete in that time.

c. If the actual distance travelled by the second car is 360 km, calculate the speed of the first car to 3 significant figures.

12. The diagram shows the graph of $y = \cos x°$, $0 \leqslant x < 360$.

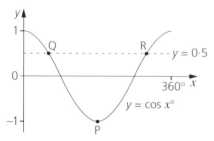

a. Write down the coordinates of point P, the minimum turning point of the graph.

b. The straight line $y = 0.5$ cuts the graph at Q and R.
Find the coordinates of Q and R.

Chapter 1 Testing your Calculation Skills

Exercise 1.1

1. 20·82
2. 82·4
3. 1087·2
4. 0·835
5. 3570
6. 34·8

Exercise 1.2

1. 5
2. −3
3. 8
4. 120
5. −18
6. −36

Exercise 1.3

1. $5\frac{3}{4}$
2. $2\frac{3}{5}$
3. $\frac{1}{6}$
4. $\frac{1}{12}$
5. $14\frac{1}{4}$
6. £230
7. 52·8 kg
8. 154·4 tonnes
9. £4·26

Exercise 1.4

1. 6
2. 20
3. 125
4. 676
5. 32
6. 27
7. $\frac{1}{9}$
8. $\frac{8}{125}$
9. $\frac{3}{4}$

Exercise 1.5

1. 350
2. 70 000
3. 38·5
4. 7·67
5. 40·0

Exercise 1.6

1. a. $2a + 6b$
b. $12x - 24y$
c. $13m - 30$
d. $2t - 11u$
e. $10x - 3y$
f. $2a - 5b$

2. a. $2(2a + b)$
b. $3(2x - 3y)$
c. $4(3x + 5y)$
d. $3(5a + 6b - 7c)$
e. $a(b + c)$
f. $x(y - z)$

Exercise 1.7

1. 8
2. −2
3. −12
4. 57·4
5. −5
6. 0·9
7. 21
8. 1·2
9. 2

Exercise 1.8

1. $\frac{9}{10}$
2. $4\frac{1}{15}$
3. $3\frac{1}{6}$
4. $-\frac{1}{30}$
5. $\frac{1}{5}$
6. $\frac{3}{14}$
7. $\frac{25}{42}$
8. $15\frac{2}{5}$
9. $\frac{7}{9}$

Exercise 1.9

1. 4·6
2. 39 600
3. 1·0
4. 0·00000693
5. 50 million (or 50 000 000)
6. 0·81

Exercise 1.10

1. a. $2\sqrt{3}$
b. $5\sqrt{2}$
c. $20\sqrt{10}$
d. $4\sqrt{5}$
e. $4\sqrt{3}$
f. 6
g. $5\sqrt{2} + 2$

2. a. a^8
b. y^5
c. z^6
d. p^2
e. $4m^6$
f. a^4b^8
g. x^2
h. a^3
i. a^3b^6

3. a. 32
b. 81
c. 25
d. $\frac{1}{32}$
e. 2
f. 10

4. a. $\frac{\sqrt{5}}{5}$
b. $5\sqrt{2}$
c. $\sqrt{2}$
d. $\frac{\sqrt{12}}{3}$ or $\frac{2\sqrt{3}}{3}$
e. $\frac{\sqrt{70}}{10}$
f. $\frac{2\sqrt{2}}{5}$
g. $12\left(2 + \sqrt{3}\right)$
h. $\sqrt{5} - \sqrt{3}$
i. $2\left(\sqrt{5} + \sqrt{2}\right)$

Answers to Exercises

Chapter 2   Formulae and Equations

Exercise 2.1

1. a. $P = 2 \times n + 1$ **b.** $y = 3x - 2$
(better $P = 2n + 1$) $y = 28$
$P = 17$ $x = 20$
$n = 11$

2. a.

h	1	2	3	4	5
m	5	9	13	17	21

  i. $m = 4h + 1$
  ii. $m = 49$
  iii. $h = 24$

b.

P	2	3	4	5
C	3	6	9	12

  i. $C = 3P - 3 = 3(P - 1)$
  ii. $C = 147$
  iii. $P = 11$
iv. No, because chains must be in multiples of 3. 52 is not a multiple of 3.

Exercise 2.2

1. a. i. 5 minutes   **ii.** 6 minutes 30 s
   iii. 14 minutes 30 s   **iv.** 12 minutes 12 s
  b. i. 50 g   **ii.** 225 g

2. a. £77
  b. £156·60
  c. £64·70

Exercise 2.3

1. $x = 3$ **2.** $x = 10$
3. $x = 9$ **4.** $x = 3$
5. $x = -9·5$ **6.** $x = 3$
7. $x < 3$ **8.** $x > -1$
9. $x < 7$

Exercise 2.4

1. $x = -1$ **2.** $t = 4$
3. $y = 2·5$ **4.** $z = 3$
5. $x = 12$ **6.** $p = 5$
7. $a = -2$ **8.** $y > -12$
9. $c < 4$ **10.** $b > 1\frac{2}{5}$
11. $x < \frac{5}{32}$

Exercise 2.5

1. $h = \dfrac{V}{\pi r^2}$ $h = 2·63$ (to 3 sf)

2. $a = \dfrac{2(s - ut)}{t^2}$ $a = 8$

3. $R = \dfrac{V}{I}$ $R = 16$

4. $b = \sqrt{a^2 - c^2}$ $b = 15$

Exercise 2.6

1. multiplied by 4

2. increased by 25%

3. a. 10% bigger   **b.** 4 times greater

Exercise 2.7

1. 0, 5   **2.** 0, 2
3. $\frac{3}{2}, -\frac{3}{2}$ **4.** 5, −5
5. 1, 5   **6.** $\frac{1}{3}$, 3
7. 1, $\frac{3}{2}$ **8.** $\frac{2}{3}$
9. $\frac{3}{2}, -\frac{2}{3}$ **10.** 12, −2
11. 5, −13   **12.** 3
13. 0, 1   **14.** 5·45, 0·55
15. 0·64, −1·24   **16.** 2·24, −0·54
17. 2·58, 1·42   **18.** 0·41, −2·41

Chapter 3   Shape

Exercise 3.1

1. $a = 55$ (straight line)
  $b = 89$ (vertically opposite)
  $c = 36$ (three angles in triangle)
  $d = 55$ (alternate to a)
  $e = 36$ (alternate to c)
  $f = 91$ (supplementary to b)

2. a. 3   **b.** 6
  c. 4

3. a.   **b.**

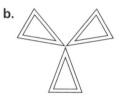

4. A(2, 4) B(4, 6) C(7, 6) D(9, 4) E(7, 2) F(4, 2)

Exercise 3.2

1. Rhombus, all sides 10 cm, BÂD and BĈD are 60°, AB̂C and AD̂C are 120°
2. Parallelogram, GH is 13 cm, EH is 8 cm, EF̂G is 80°, HÊF and HĜF are 100°
3. Equilateral triangle, all sides 15 cm, all angles 60°
4. Kite, PS is 5 cm, QR is 9 cm, QR̂S is 80°, QP̂S is 140°, PQ̂R and PŜR are 70°

Exercise 3.3

1. 35 cm   **2.** 5400 m
3. 0·75 litres   **4.** 4 litres
5. 460 mm   **6.** 53 kg
7. 40 km   **8.** 2900 kg

Exercise 3.4

1. 1612 cm²   **2.** 23·04 m²
3. 450 cm²   **4.** 1 m²
5. 63 mm²   **6.** 310 m²
7. 315 m²   **8.** 103 cm²
9. 806 cm²

Exercise 3.5

1. 45·1 cm, 44·9 cm
2. 4·65 m, 4·55 m
3. 62°, 58°
4. 455 g, 445 g
5. 27·2 mm, 26·8 mm
6. 351 ml, 349 ml

Exercise 3.6

1. Square (based) pyramid
2. 40 m

Exercise 3.7

1. 27 cm³, 0·027 litres
2. 7200 cm³, 7·2 litres
3. (cross-section $\pi \times 8^2$) 8244 cm³ (to nearest cm³), 8·244 litres
4. (cross-section 186 cm²) 2976 cm³, 2·976 litres
5. (cross-section 0·52 m²) 1·04 m³, 1040 litres
6. **a.** 40 (8 × 5)
   b. 6 (some space left)
   c. 6·48 litres (240 × 27 cm³)
   d. because the box has space left at the top
7. 2280 cm²

Exercise 3.8

1. 56 400 cm³ (to 3 sf)
2. 40 cm
3. 400 m³ (400 000 litres)
4. 17·0 cm (to 3 sf)

Chapter 4   Arithmetic

Exercise 4.1

1. **a.** 35 000   **b.** 7 000 000
   c. 462   **d.** 258 000
   e. 0·003   **f.** 0·00046
   g. 0·01374   **h.** 0·00000754
   i. 4·4
2. **a.** 5×10^3 **b.** $8·3 \times 10^4$
   c. $2·7 \times 10^5$ **d.** 2×10^6
   e. $5·7 \times 10^{-2}$ **f.** $6·2 \times 10^{-3}$
   g. $9·69 \times 10^{-2}$ **h.** 2×10^{-1}
   i. 5×10^{-1}

Exercise 4.2

1. £39·99
2. £32·78
3. £139·05
4. 1030 pupils
5. 36 000 fish
6. £13 905·00
7. £256·15

Exercise 4.3

1. **a.** £30   **b.** £530
2. **a.** £14·40   **b.** £254·40
3. **a.** £56·25   **b.** £4556·25
4. **a.** £40   **b.** £12 040
5. **a.** £7·43   **b.** £667·43

Exercise 4.4

1. **a.** 3 hours 30 minutes
   b. 6 hours 45 minutes
   c. 2 hours 18 minutes
2. **a.** 4·25 hours
   b. 7·33 hours (approximately)
   c. 1·8 hours
3. **a.** 0720   **b.** 1812
   c. 0121 the next day   **d.** 1730
4. **a.** 60 mph   **b.** 64·5 km/h
   c. 72 km/h   **d.** 50 mph
5. 107·9 km
6. 168 m
7. 5 hours
8. 35 hours

Exercise 4.5

1. £52·80
2. £49 000
3. £450

Exercise 4.6

1. £5627·54
2. £5860·66

Chapter 5   Graphs and Functions

Exercise 5.1

1. about 4 minutes after arriving
2. after about 17 minutes
3. the longer race
4. no

Exercise 5.2

1. **a.** At 1500
   b. 45 minutes
   c. 1 hour from when it set out
   (or 1 hr 45 minutes from when the engine failed)

Answers to Exercises

Exercise 5.2 (cont.)

2. a.

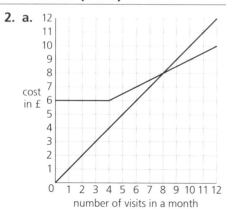
number of visits in a month

b. 8 visits

c. If you're going to go more than 8 times a month the membership card will make it cheaper.

3. a. (6, 0) and (0, 1·5)

b. second row is $\boxed{y \mid -3 \ -1 \ \ 1 \ \ 3 \ \ 5}$

c.

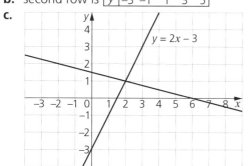
$y = 2x - 3$

d. (2, 1)

Exercise 5.3

1. Line **A** **a.** −1   **b.** (0, 1)   **c.** $y = -x + 1$
Line **B** **a.** 3   **b.** (0, −5)   **c.** $y = 3x - 5$
Line **C** **a.** $\frac{1}{2}$ **b.** (0, −3)   **c.** $y = \frac{1}{2}x - 3$

2.

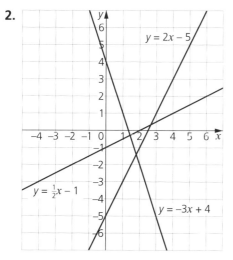
$y = 2x - 5$
$y = \frac{1}{2}x - 1$
$y = -3x + 4$

3. a. $y = 2x - 5$ **b.** $y = -2x - \frac{9}{2}$
c. $y = -6x + 14$

Exercise 5.4

1. a. $(x + 5)(x - 1)$ **b.** $x = -2$
   c. (0, −5)   **d.** −9

2. $f(0) = 1$, $f(3) = 19$

3. −3

4. −15 and 5

Exercise 5.5

1. $x = 2$, $y = 0$
2. $x = -2$, $y = 1$
3. $x = -1$, $y = 1$
4. $x = -3$, $y = 4$

Exercise 5.6

1. A(1, 3), B(−1, $\frac{1}{3}$)
2. C(3, 2), D(−1, −6)

Exercise 5.7

1. 2
2. none
3. −11

Exercise 5.8

5·32 and −1·32

Chapter 6   Maps, Plans and Similar Shapes

Exercise 6.1

1. a. 8·5 cm   **b.** 4·6 cm
   c. 8·6 cm   **d.** 6 cm

2. a. 150 km   **b.** 360 m
   c. 420 m   **d.** 390 km

3. a. 1:1000   **b.** 1:10 000 000
   c. 1:200 000   **d.** 1:4 000 000

Exercise 6.2

Any answers involving drawing or measuring will be acceptable. Your answers might not be exact, but they should be within 2 mm and 2°.

1. a. 14·6 km   **b.** 250°

2. a. 5 km, 150°
   b. 4·1 km, 060°
   c. 6·5 km, 110°
   d. circumference of a circle, centre R, radius 3 cm

Exercise 6.3

1. $h = 9$ cm
2. 526·5 cm²

Exercise 6.4

1. 1·8 m   **2.** $a = 4·1$ m, $b = 6·5$ m
3. 5·1 m

(Answers to the above are correct to 1 dp – if you are inaccurate, check you have not been rounding off in the middle of the calculations.)

4. 2315 ml   **5.** 56·25 g

Chapter 7   Proportion and Variation

Exercise 7.1

1. 5 days
2. 3·2 cm
3. 4·5 km/h

Exercise 7.2

1. a. 1:6   **b.** 12:7
   c. 3:8

2. a. £1·75 and £3·25   **b.** 750 ml and 250 ml

Exercise 7.3

1. 50 g silk, 67 g cotton
2. total budget £89 000 000
    transport costs £17 000 000

Exercise 7.4

1. 12
2. 28·8 newtons
3. The graph is a straight line going through (0, 0).

Exercise 7.5

1. 1·5 litres

2. For each pair of values xy is the same, 30.

3. $I = \dfrac{18}{d^2}$. When $d = 2$ cm, $I = 4·5$ W/m²

4. a. $W = \dfrac{Ld^2}{12}$ or $\dfrac{1}{12}Ld^2$
   b. $W = 800$ g

5. 313K (to nearest kelvin)

6. Force between Venus and the Sun will be a quarter, or 25%, of force between Mercury and the Sun.

7. a 45 m (2·25 times as far as A)
   b. A 40 m, B 90 m

Chapter 8   Triangles and Trigonometry

Exercise 8.1

1. 45·2 km
2. AB = 6·4 cm, BC = 12·6 cm
3. 5·2 m
4. 8·9 units

Exercise 8.2

1. 50·3°
2. 12·1 km
3. 1·1 m (to 1 dp)

Exercise 8.3

1. 20·9 m
2. 3·9 m
3. $h = 6 \tan 23° = 2·546…$ which is lower than the required 'target'.

Exercise 8.4

1. 49·5 and 130·5
   (second answer is 180 – 49·5)
2. 55·9 and 304·1
3. 76·9 and 256·9
4. 233·1 and 306·9
   (These can be obtained from 180 + 53·1 and 360 – 53·1.)
5. 98·0 and 262·0
6. 96·0 and 276·0
7. 36·9 and 143·1
8. 63·4 and 243·4
9. 113·6 and 246·4

Exercise 8.5

1. 11·9

2. 4·53

3. 78·5

4. 43·0 square units

5. 42·4°

6. 2·73 km

7. a. 124 km   **b.** 317°

8. a. 95·6 m²   **b.** 11·9 litres

Exercise 8.6

1. $y = \cos x° + 3$

2. $a = -2$, $b = 2$

3. $k = 3$, $c = 0·5$

4. maximum –3, minimum –5

5. 180°

6. a. 16·9 hours
   b. 17 hours and 7 hours
   c. M = 5·67, by solving
     $12 + 5 \sin (30M – 80)° = 17$
     Notice that 5·67 months means about two thirds of the way through June, which is of course when the Northern hemisphere has most daylight hours.
   d. 5:10 pm,
     since when M = 10, H = 8·79 hours.
   e. M = 2·67 and 8·67,
     by solving $12 + 5 \sin (30M – 80)° = 12$.
     Notice that these answers fit with spring and autumn equinoxes in March and September.

Answers to Exercises

Chapter 9   The Circle

Exercise 9.1

1.   area   circumference
   a. 12·6 cm²   12·6 cm
   b. 1590 m²   141 m
   c. 4·37 m²   7·41 m

2. 18·1 cm

3. 97·7 m

4. a. 69·1 cm   b. 81·7 mm
   c. 5·57 m

5. 151 cm

6. 339 cm²

Exercise 9.2

1. a. 90° (angle where tangent meets radius)
   b. 30°

2. a. isosceles   b. 80°
   c. 10°

3. a. angle in a semicircle
   b. angle BD̂E   c. 79°

Exercise 9.3

1. 21·2 cm²
2. 13·8 cm² (sector 22·08 cm², triangle 8·31 cm²)
3. 5·24 cm
4. 57·3°
5. 43·8 cm
6. 134 cm (chord 41·7 cm, arc 92·3 cm)

Chapter 10 Statistics

Exercise 10.1

1. a.
Number	Tally	Frequency
33	I	1
34	I	1
35	I	1
36	ЖН	5
37	II	2
38	III	3
39	III	3
40	III	3
41	I	1
	Total	20

b.
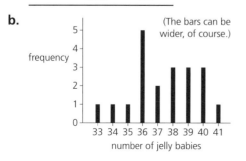
(The bars can be wider, of course.)

2.
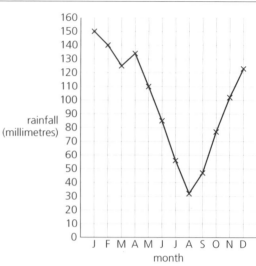

3.
```
3 | 2 8                6 | 1 represents 61,
4 | 5 5 6 7 8 9            n = 24
5 | 3 3 6 7
6 | 1 6 9
7 | 0 4 5 8 9
8 | 2 3 8
9 | 1
```

4. a. 1A: 148 cm; 2A: 150 cm
       2 cm taller in 2nd year.
   b. Range is the same, 43 cm, for both years
       (128 cm up to 171 cm). This must mean
       that the shortest and the tallest students
       didn't grow at all during the year.

5. a. £35 000
   b. 1992, £50 000 at the end of 1992
   c. During 1993 and 1994
   d. Prices rose during the first three years, fell
       during the next two years, were stable for
       two years before rising again.

Exercise 10.2

1. a. **A**: 37·4   **B**: 98·4 mm   **C**: 61·9
   b. **A**: 37·5   **B**: 106 mm   **C**: 59
   c. **A**: 8   **B**: 118 mm   **C**: 59
   d. **A**: 36

2. 11 years

3. a. $\frac{1}{6}$ b. $\frac{1}{2}$
   c. $\frac{2}{5}$ d. $\frac{4}{11}$

Exercise 10.3

1. a. 32 mpg   b. 1·0 litre
   c. Negative correlation: bigger engines tend
       to have poorer fuel economy.

1. d.

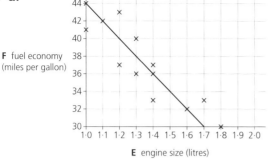

F fuel economy (miles per gallon)

E engine size (litres)

Line should be approximately in the direction shown in the diagram above, with at least three points on each side of it.

e. About 34 mpg

(It depends exactly where you put your line.)

2.

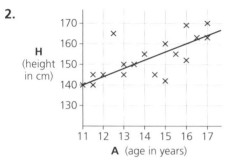

H (height in cm)

A (age in years)

Your line should be close to the line shown and have at least five points on either side.

The graph shows positive correlation – the older the person, the taller he or she tends to be.

Exercise 10.4

1.

		Cumulative Frequency
33	...	1
34	...	2
35	...	3
36	...	8
37	...	10
38	...	13
39	...	16
40	...	19
41	...	20

This is the extra column you should have added to the table in Exercise 10.1, question **1**.

2. 39, 36
3. 1·5
4. 76·5 and 47·5, 14·5

Exercise 10.5

1.

2. a. 13, 7, 22, 22
  b. 5 times (lower quartile is 10, so 25% of the sessions)
  c. Usually less (since median is less than 15)

3.

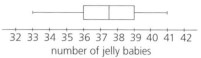

number of jelly babies

4.

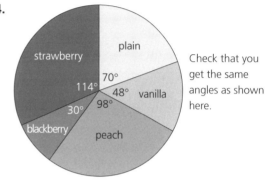

Check that you get the same angles as shown here.

Exercise 10.6

1. $a = -20$, $b = 64$ $F = -20E + 64$
2. $p = 4$, $q = 96$ $H = 4A + 96$

Exercise 10.7

1. a. 26   **b.** 17·7

2. a. £1·07   **b.** £0·35

3. a. 7·5 minutes and 2·2 minutes
  b. The older men were considerably less fit, and there was more variation in fitness amongst the older men.

Answers to General Practice Exam A

General Exam A Paper 1

1. a. **5·6**
   b. **0·73**
   c. **254 kg**
   d. **1620**

2. a. **£3·75**
   b. $\frac{1}{4}$

3. a. Any four of these: 060, 240, 420, 480, 600, 660, 840
   b. The only even prime is 2, so **420**.

4. Most in one roll = 288.
   Most on four rolls = 4×288 = **1152**

5. Total 14°. Divide by 7 to get mean = **2°**

6. a. 300 g $\Rightarrow$ 6 minutes,
   1000 g $\Rightarrow$ 20 minutes,
   4000 g $\Rightarrow$ 80 minutes
   b. $T = \frac{M}{50}$

7. a.

week 1		week 2	
6 2	1	0 3 4	
5 1	2	9	
	3	9	
9 6	4		
6	5	8	
	6	2	
n = 7		n = 7	

   2 | 1 represents
   21 people

   b. **Wednesday**. This is because the numbers on Wednesday are higher than on Monday, Tuesday and Thursday. (Friday night is the start of the weekend.)

8. **a** and **b.**

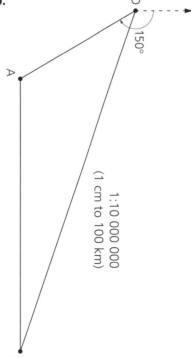

   c. DB = 10·6 cm on plan, and the scale is 1 cm to 100 km, so real distance is **1060 km**, and the bearing measures **109°**.

General Exam A Paper 2

1. **5·64218 $\times$ 10⁸**

2. 109 505 ÷ 523·8 = £209·06. This is less than £245 so yes, it would have been cheaper in Greece.

3. a. hours × frequency
   0
   7
   8
   27
   12
   25
   _____
   total   79 hours
   total frequency 31 days
   mean = 79 ÷ 31 = **2·55 hours** (to 2 dp)
   b. highest – lowest = 5 – 0 = **5**

4. a. Add: 121 + 208 + 314 + 201 = **844 km**
   b. 844 × £0·36 = **£303·84**

5. a. Let x stand for Rory's amount in pounds. So Helen raised $x + 8$, Ken raised $x + 5$
   Add: $x + (x + 8) + (x + 5) = 79$
   b. $3x + 13 = 79$
   $3x = 66$
   $x = 22$
   So Rory raised £22 and Ken raised **£27**

6. a.

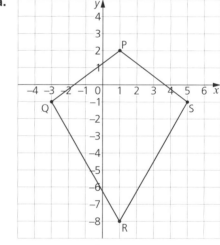

   b. along 4, up 3, so $\frac{3}{4}$ **or 0·75**
   c. base PR = 10, height = 4.
   Area = $\frac{1}{2} \times$ base $\times$ height = **20 unit²**

7. a.

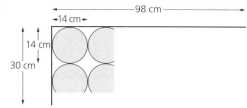

think: how many 14s in 98?
how many 14s in 30?

radius = 7 cm, so diameter = 14 cm
98 ÷ 14 = 7, 30 ÷ 14 ~ 2
(There'll be a strip left which cannot be used.) So 7 × 2 = **14 lids** can be cut.

b. Area $= 14 \times \pi r^2$
$= 14 \times \pi \times 7 \times 7$
$= 2155 \cdot 13\ldots$ cm²
Area of whole sheet $= 98 \times 30$
$= 2940$ cm²
Amount wasted $= 2940 - 2155 \cdot 13\ldots$
$= \textbf{785 cm}^2$
(to the nearest cm²)

8.

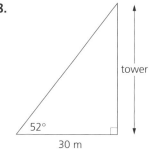

If h stands for height, $\tan 52° = \frac{h}{30}$
so $h = 30 \times \tan 52° = \textbf{38·4 metres}$

9. a. $V = \frac{1}{3} \times \pi \times 8 \times 8 \times 20 = \textbf{1340 cm}^3$ (to the nearest cm³)

b. cube of side 12 cm has volume $= 12^3$
$= 12 \times 12 \times 12 = 1728$ cm³, which is more than 1340 cm³, so the cube cannot be made from the cone.

10. 40 white balloons out of 120 altogether, so
$\frac{40}{120} = \frac{1}{3}$.

11. For 1 year, I = 4·5% of £9500 = £427·50
4 months is $\frac{1}{3}$ of a year, so divide by 3 to get
£142·50

12. diagonals are perpendicular: use Pythagoras in the small triangles
upper part of diagonal: $\sqrt{18^2 - 14^2}$
lower part: $\sqrt{35^2 - 14^2}$
total $= 11 \cdot 31\ldots + 32 \cdot 08\ldots = \textbf{43·4 cm}$ (to 1 dp)

13. a. 95 extra pupils, $\frac{95}{964} = \textbf{9·9\%}$ (to 1 dp)

b. 964 + 95 = 1059, so **yes**, over 1000

c. 95 ÷ 20 = 4·75, so **5** extra teachers

General Exam B Paper 1

1. a. **15·26**
b. **7·05 kg**
c. **2·48**
d. **−42**

2. 5 − 8 = **−3˚C**

3. a. $\frac{3}{5}$ of 640 = **384**
b. Add $\frac{3}{5}$ and $\frac{1}{4}$, by changing both to twentieths, making $\frac{17}{20}$. So $\frac{3}{20}$ opted out.

4. a. **67°** (alternate angle with BÔC, parallel lines)
b. **23°** (BD̂A = 90° [angle in semicircle] then angle sum in triangle BDA)
c. **23°** (OB̂C = 90° [between tangent and radius] then angle sum in triangle BOC)

5. a. common factor $3x$, **$3x(1 − 2y)$**
b. Next line $4x = 8$, so **$x = 2$**

6.

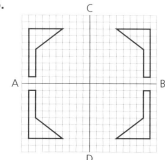

7. **0·0000256 m**

8. Angle for sector representing Cristina is 120°, which is $\frac{1}{3}$ of 360°, so share is $\frac{1}{3}$ of 48 votes: **16 votes**

General Exam B Paper 2

1. **4** is the mode as it occurs eight times, more than any other number.

2. Scale factor for length is $\frac{15}{10}$, or 1·5. Area factor is $1·5^2 = 2·25$. Multiply 140 by 2·25: **315 cm²**

3. a. Butter will be $\frac{1}{4}$ of the flour's weight, **140 g**
b. $\frac{560}{200} = 2·8$,
so he can make 2·8 × 15 scones: **42**

Answers to General Practice Exam B and Credit Practice Exam A

4. a. $18 \times £27\cdot85 = £501\cdot30$. Add on deposit: **£556·30**

   b. Hire purchase extra: £66·30.
Percentage: $\frac{66\cdot30}{490} = 0\cdot135... = $ **13·5%** (to 1 dp)

5. Total cost £403·70. Dividing that by 18 gives 22·42… so **23 days'** hire will cover costs

6. gradient = vertical ÷ horizontal
$$= 40 \div 320$$
$$= \textbf{0·125 or } \tfrac{1}{8}.$$

7. a. 320 cm – (2 × 68) cm leaves **184 cm**
= **1·84 m**

   b. $C = \pi d$.
Length $= \pi \times 1\cdot36 + \pi \times 1\cdot84$
$= $ **10·05 m** (to 2 dp)

8. Draw in line of symmetry. Work in one of the right-angled triangles.
$\tan x° = \frac{2\cdot8}{2}$ so $x = $ **54·5** (to 1 dp)

9. a.

x	0	1	2	3	4	5
y	–3	–1	1	3	5	7

   b. $y = 2x - 3$
   c. $n = 2 \times (-5) - 3 = -10 - 3 = $ **–13**

10. a. $2 \times 5 + 4^2 = 10 + 16 = $ **26**
    b. $14 + a^2 = 15$, so $a = $ **1**

11. $D = kV^2$, $k = \frac{160}{80^2} = 0\cdot025$ so $D = 0\cdot025V^2$.
$D = 0\cdot025 \times 120^2 = $ **360 metres**

12. The shape can be rearranged into a rectangle: remove the right-angled triangle at the right side and move it into the space at the left side. Area = $3\cdot5 \times 3\cdot1 = $ **10·85 cm²**

13. Commission = £432 and this is 2% of sales, so 1% = £216, and 100% is **£21 600**.

Credit Exam A Paper 1

1. a. **32·5** (remember, × and ÷ before + and –)
   b. $\frac{3}{5}$ of $\frac{5}{6} = \frac{3}{5} \times \frac{5}{6} = \frac{1}{2}$

2. a. $-12 - 16 = $ **–28**   **b.** $-9 + \frac{0}{4} = $ **–9**

3. $6x^2 - 10xy + 15xy - 25y^2$
$= \textbf{6}x^2 + \textbf{5}xy - \textbf{25}y^2$

4. a. factorise: $(4x + 1)(2x - 3) = 0$
$$4x = -1 \quad 2x = 3$$
$$x = -\tfrac{1}{4} \quad x = \tfrac{3}{2}$$
   b. $x = 9(8 + x)$ that is, multiplying both sides by $(8 + x)$, leading to $x = $ **–9**

5. $T = \frac{KW^2}{X} = 24$
substitute 2X for X: T will be halved, so **T = 12**

6. $f(4) = 4^2 + \frac{1}{4} = \mathbf{16\tfrac{1}{4}}$

7. $\sqrt{50} = \sqrt{25} \times \sqrt{2} = \mathbf{5\sqrt{2}}$

8. $\frac{1}{2a^2}$

9. a. difference of two squares $(x - 3)(x + 3)$
   b. $\frac{x^2 - 9}{2x + 6} = \frac{(x - 3)(x + 3)}{2(x + 3)}$ [then cancel]
$$= \frac{x - 3}{2}$$

10. Height of larger jug is 2 times height of smaller jug, so scale factor for volume is 2^3. Volume of large jug = $0\cdot4 \times 2^3 = $ **3·2 litres**

Credit Exam A Paper 2

1. a. 14 pieces of data, arrange in order, average of 7th and 8th pieces,
$(27 + 34) \div 2 = $ **30·5**
4th value is lower quartile: **18**
11th value is upper quartile: **46**

   b.
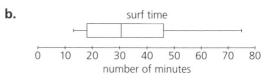

2. $E = (8 \times 3 \times 3) \times 10^{(-3 + 8 + 8)}$
$= 72 \times 10^{13}$
$= \mathbf{7\cdot2 \times 10^{14}}$
(You can work this out on your calculator.)

3. a. **35**
   b. $d = 2s$, so put $2s$ in the place of d in the formula and solve it for s.
You'll get $s^2 - 7s = 0$, and eventually $s = 0$ and $s = $ **7**.
To really impress the examiner explain (briefly!) why $s = 0$ can't be the right answer.
   c. If $d = s$, put s in place of d in the formula and solve to find s. ($s = 5$)
Try the formula with a value of s greater than 5 and a value less than 5. The answer is that all values less than 5 give more sides than diagonals, ie **3 and 4** (since 1 and 2 won't give a polygon at all). And yes, a triangle is a polygon.

4. In the right-angled triangle, one
length is known (6 km) and one
angle can be worked out
$(63° - 52° = 11°)$.
Use sin 11° and the
required length, d, will work out at 1·14... km,
which is greater than 1 km. So the ship will
not approach the lighthouse too closely if it
continues on its present course.

5. a. $A = 4 \times \pi \times 4^2 = 201·06...$ m², so area
of hemisphere is **100·5 m²** (to 1 dp)
   b. Area of roof = $9 \times 9 = 81$ m²
Area covered by hemisphere
$= \pi \times 4^2 = 50·26...$ m²
so area to be painted = **30·7 m²** (to 1 dp)
   c. Area of four walls = $4 \times 9^2 = 324$ m²
Total area = $324 + 30·73... + 100·53...$
$= 455·26... = $ **455 m²** (to 3 sf)

6. £45 000 is 100% + 18% = 118%.
So 1% is $(45\,000 ÷ 118) = 381·35...$,
giving 100% = $381·35... \times 100 = 38\,135·59...$
so flat cost **£38 000** to nearest £ thousand.

7. a. Total = 56, mean = $\frac{56}{7} =$ **8**
range = $18 - 0 =$ **18**.
   b. $\sum x^2 = 758$, $(\sum x)^2 = 56^2 = 3136$, $n = 7$.
Substituting these into a standard deviation
formula gives **s = 7·2 knots** (to 1 dp).
(You can use the other standard deviation formula
if you prefer.)

8. Other angles in triangle are both 70°.
Tangents are perpendicular to radii. Four
angles of quadrilateral total 360°. $a° =$ **110°**

9. If V is multiplied by 3, V² is multiplied by 9.
So air drag will be **multiplied by 9**, as it
varies with V².

10. The angles of the triangle work out at 110°,
43° and 27°. Only one side is known so the
sine rule should be used, leading to
d = 414 metres (to 3 sf)

11. a. $£20 + (50 \times £0·40) =$ **£40**
   b. $C = 20 + (t - 30) \times 0·40$ or
$C = 20 + 0·4(t - 30) =$ **8 + 0·4t**
   c. **C = 18 + 0·35t**
   d. Solve $8 + 0·4t = 18 + 0·35t$
giving $0·05t = 10$, so **t = 200 minutes**

12. a. Cosine graph, period 180° so **a = 2**, and
amplitude 4, so **k = 4**
(Graph shows $y = 4 \cos 2x°$)
   b. $\tan x° = -\frac{7}{3}$ Related angle in 1st
quadrant: 66·8°. Tangent is negative in
2nd and 4th quadrants,
so $x = 180 - 66·8$ or $x = 360 - 66·8$,
answers: **x = 113·2 or 293·2** (to 1 dp)

Credit Exam B Paper 1

1. a. $\dfrac{8\frac{2}{5} \times 5}{1\frac{1}{5} \times 5} = \dfrac{42}{6} =$ **7**
   b. **−1·9** (remember × and ÷ before + and −)

2. a. **−98**   **b.** $-3\frac{2}{3}$

3. a. $-4\sqrt{5}$ **b.** x^7

4. Triangles OBC and ADB are both right-angled.
(See answers to General Exam B Paper 1,
question **4** for reasons.)
Since angle $O\hat{B}C = 90°$ (tangent and radius)
then angle $C\hat{O}B = 90° - x$.
Angle $C\hat{O}B =$ angle $O\hat{B}D$ (alternate angles)
so **y = 90 − x** (or $y + x = 90$)

5. $\tan x° = \dfrac{\sin x°}{\cos x°} = \dfrac{\frac{1}{\sqrt{3}}}{\frac{2\sqrt{2}}{\sqrt{3}}} = \dfrac{\frac{1}{\sqrt{3}} \times \sqrt{3}}{\frac{2\sqrt{2}}{\sqrt{3}} \times \sqrt{3}} = \dfrac{1}{2\sqrt{2}}$.
Now rationalise the denominator:
$\dfrac{1}{2\sqrt{2}} = \dfrac{1 \times \sqrt{2}}{2\sqrt{2} \times \sqrt{2}} = \dfrac{\sqrt{2}}{4}$
Well done if you didn't need any help – this question is
really too hard for Credit level.

6. a. Common factor is a^2b $a^2b(1 - ab)$
   b. Multiply both sides by x to remove the
fraction, then arrange in standard
quadratic form: $2x^2 - 7x - 4 = 0$, giving
$(2x + 1)(x - 4) = 0$
so $x = -\frac{1}{2}$ or **x = 4**

7. a. $f(a^2) = 3(a^2)^2 =$ **3a⁴**
   b. $\dfrac{3x^2 + x - 10}{2x + 4} = \dfrac{(3x - 5)(x + 2)}{2x + 4}$ [by factorising]
$= \dfrac{3x - 5}{2}$ [by cancelling]

8. $F = 6 + \dfrac{5}{M}$
$F - 6 = \dfrac{5}{M}$ [by subtracting 6 from both sides]
$M(F - 6) = 5$ [by multiplying by M]
$M = \dfrac{5}{F - 6}$ [by dividing both sides by (F − 6)]

9. Median is **41**, upper and lower quartiles are
47 and 36 so semi-interquartile range is
$\frac{1}{2}(47 - 36) =$ **5·5**.

Answers to Credit Practice Exam B

Credit Exam B Paper 2

1. The best way to do this is
$(2 \times 10^6) \times 1{\cdot}15^3 = 3{\cdot}041... \times 10^6$
$= \mathbf{3{\cdot}0 \times 10^6}$ (to 2 sf)
If you find this confusing, you can work out each hour's increase separately. (Page 23 of *Standard Grade Maths Revision Notes* may help.)

2. a.

Age	Number of girls	Cumulative frequency
5	2	2
6	1	3
7	3	6
8	4	10
9	4	14
10	6	20
11	8	28
12	19	47
13	3	50
14	1	51
15	1	52

b. up to age 8

3. $12 - y - 5 < 3$
$7 - y < 3$ [now add y to both sides]
$7 < 3 + y$
so $4 < y$ giving $\mathbf{y > 4}$

4. Intercept on vertical axis is 220. Gradient is negative and $\frac{220}{40}$ gives 5·5 so gradient is −5·5. Equation $\mathbf{V = -5{\cdot}5t + 220}$.

5. a. At the net $x = 5$ so calculate
$H(5) = 1 + 0{\cdot}8 \times 5 - 0{\cdot}08 \times 5^2 = \mathbf{3\ metres}$
b. $1 = 1 + 0{\cdot}8x - 0{\cdot}08x^2$
$0 = 0{\cdot}8x - 0{\cdot}08x^2$
$0 = x(0{\cdot}8 - 0{\cdot}08x)$
so $x = 0$ (this is when the ball is hit)
or $x = 10$. So the distance is **10 metres**

6.

Modal score: the most common, so **2**.

7. Equal ratios of sides $\frac{EF}{5{\cdot}7} = \frac{5{\cdot}9+3{\cdot}1}{5{\cdot}9}$
so EF = **8·7** (to 1 dp)

8. Quadratic formula, a = 1, b = −3, c = −8.
so $x = \mathbf{4{\cdot}7\ or\ -1{\cdot}7}$

9. a. Use converse of Pythagoras:
$a^2 + b^2 = 52{\cdot}2$ but $c^2 = 64$ so triangle is not right-angled and so shape is not a semicircle.
b. Use trig in the small right-angled triangle to find x: hypotenuse is a radius
$(\cos x = \frac{4}{4\cdot1})\ x° = \mathbf{12{\cdot}7°}$ (to 1 dp)
c. Angle at centre of segment
$= 180 - (2 \times 12{\cdot}7) = 154{\cdot}6°$.
Length of arc $= \frac{154{\cdot}6}{360}$ of circumference
$= \mathbf{11{\cdot}1\ metres}$ (to 1 dp)

10. All the angles of the triangle are known. Only one side is known so use the Sine Rule to find either AC or AB. Then use SOHCAHTOA in the right-angled triangle on one or other side of perpendicular through C.
20·5 metres

11. a. Use the formula Time $= \frac{D}{S}$ giving
$\mathbf{T = \frac{500}{x}\ hours}$
b. D = ST so D $= 30 \times \frac{500}{x} = \frac{\mathbf{15\ 000}}{x}$ **km**
c. $\frac{15\ 000}{x} = 360$ so $x = \frac{15\ 000}{360} = 41{\cdot}66...$
$= \mathbf{41{\cdot}7\ km/h}$ (to 3 sf)

12. a. **(180, −1)**
b. Solve $\cos x° = 0{\cdot}5$. Calculator easily gives $x = 60$, so **Q(60, 0·5)**.
From the symmetry of the cosine graph, **R(300, 0·5)**